Hinges of Administration

Hinges of Administration

A survey of the characteristics of hospital administrative and clerical staff

J R Griffith BLitt MA FHA

Professor of Hospital Administration, University of New South Wales
formerly Director, Nuffield Centre for Hospital and
Health Services Studies, University of Leeds

E T Rees BA DSA AHA

Assistant Secretary to the Board of Governors,
United Leeds Hospitals

Published for the Nuffield Provincial Hospitals Trust
by the Oxford University Press   1963
London New York Toronto

Oxford University Press, Amen House, London E.C.4

GLASGOW NEW YORK TORONTO MELBOURNE WELLINGTON
BOMBAY CALCUTTA MADRAS KARACHI KUALA LUMPUR
CAPE TOWN IBADAN NAIROBI ACCRA

PRINTED IN GREAT BRITAIN BY THE WHITEFRIARS PRESS LTD., LONDON AND TONBRIDGE

Acknowledgements

This research and report were made possible by a generous grant by the Nuffield Provincial Hospitals Trust for which we are much indebted. In particular we should like to thank Sir David Lindsay Keir and Mr. Gordon McLachlan, the Secretary of the Trust, for all the help and advice we have received from them throughout our work.

We are also indebted to the senior hospital administrators and the administrative and clerical staff of the four hospital regions—Liverpool, North-East Metropolitan, Sheffield and the South-Western— whose readiness to answer questions provided us with the material on which this report is based.

We were greatly assisted in various ways by many organizations and individuals. They are too numerous to list here but nevertheless we fully appreciate their contributions and we wish again to express our thanks to them all.

The Board of Governors of the United Leeds Hospitals and the Leeds (A) Hospital Management Committee kindly allowed us the use of punch-card and sorting machines, and members of the staff of these authorities assisted us in operating the machines.

Finally we wish to record our appreciation of such valuable help received from Mr. Alex Barr, Statistician of the Oxford Regional Hospital Board, Mr. Hugh Clegg, Fellow of Nuffield College, Oxford, and our colleagues in Leeds—Mr. Keith Barnard, Mr. John Dann and Mr. William Miles.

The typing and some of the coding, checking and tabulation were done by Mrs. Horrox assisted by Mrs. Pemberton and Miss Hughes, to whom, and also to Ruth Griffith, we are most grateful for their tolerance and patience.

JOHN GRIFFITH
TIMOTHY REES

Foreword

The study of which this book is a report was an early outcome of the Trust's decision in 1957 to sponsor a pilot training scheme in hospital administration based on the Adult Education Department of the University of Leeds. The objects of this pilot scheme were not only drawn to include experiments with various types of courses for administrators in the hospital service, but also to try to discover the probable demand for, as distinct from the requirements of, such courses. Since there was no precise data available about the educational standards of administrative staffs in the hospital service, a survey was begun which was eventually extended to cover four Regions, in an attempt not merely to get an indication of the educational levels, but also to estimate the promotional chances, the prospects of movement and the annual recruitment needs for the next 10 years. As a direct consequence it was hoped that a picture of the training requirements would emerge.

Many aspects of the National Health Service since 1948 have been the subject of enquiry by a multitude of committees. It is open to doubt whether a committee, without having available the right kind of data or, in its absence, without commissioning properly mounted and directed research, including an independent evaluation of what has passed before can come to any worthwhile conclusions which can stand up to the rigorous scrutiny which our sophisticated times demand.

At the time of writing yet another committee, appointed by the Minister of Health, under the chairmanship of Sir Stephen Lycett Green, is enquiring into 'the present arrangements for recruitment, training and promotion of administrative and clerical staffs in the hospital service . . .'. The results of the research reported upon in this book have been made available in full to this committee at their specific request. It is surely evident that there can be no sufficient national and regional policy unless such surveys, adequately developed as to method and purpose, are more widely undertaken by the hospital authorities concerned, and the results examined in the light of existing circumstances.

This study, however, was designed only to reveal part of the picture, the whole perspective of which can be seen only if the administrative and executive content of the posts as presently established are painted in their true colours. Only if this is done and the consequential conclusions drawn can one hope to proceed to answer the full question

'How much training for what?' To some it may appear that even allowing for the subjective element the facts are disquieting for the future; although to others who are aware of the stirrings elsewhere, it might be that they indicate no more disturbing features than those to which other institutions and professions are currently subject.

In publishing this report the Trust is not itself committed to the observations made by Professor Griffith and Mr. Rees in their Epilogue. The factual part of this book should, however, stimulate those concerned with the administration of the hospital service to re-examine the basic hypotheses of the present entry and career structure of the service in relation to the training arrangements. Above all, if such an examination should lead to philosophizing about the administration of the service and an appraisal of what its real needs are, a useful purpose will have been served.

Nuffield Provincial Hospitals Trust   GORDON McLACHLAN
3 Prince Albert Road   *Secretary to the Governing Trustees*
London, N.W.1
April 1963

x

Contents

List of Appendices

Definitions

Administrative and Clerical Staff means hospital authorities' staff who come within the purview of the NHS Administrative and Clerical Staffs Whitley Council excluding 'special grades', e.g. Catering Officers, Laundry Managers, etc.

Hospital service: For the purposes of the survey the term 'hospital service' includes service in an authority set up by Part II of the National Health Service Act 1946 (Regional Hospital Boards, Boards of Governors and Hospital Management Committees) and employment in the former voluntary and local government hospitals and, where this is applicable, in Ministry of Pensions hospitals, and with local authority departments and bodies such as Hospital Contributory Schemes which resulted in a person being transferred to the NHS hospital service in 1947 or 1948.

NHS hospital service in Appendices 10 and 11 refers solely to service in an authority set up by Part II of the National Health Service Act 1946.

'the Service' = the hospital service.

'the Ministry' = the Ministry of Health.

Categories of Staff (see Appendix 2.i for a description of the staff grading structure).

For the purposes of the Survey, staff are divided into seven categories:

*D.1—includes all designated officers with minimum salaries of £2,000 p.a. or over.

*D.2—includes all designated officers with minimum salaries between £1,500 and £1,999 p.a.

*D.3—includes all designated officers with minimum salaries under £1,500 p.a.

SA—staff paid on the senior administrative grade salary scale.

GA—staff paid on the general administrative grade salary scale.

HC—staff paid on the higher clerical grade salary scale and also Personal Secretaries and Supervisors paid on this scale.

* The salaries to which these categories relate were those in force at the time of the Survey 1960–61.

C—staff paid on the clerical grade salary scale and Personal Secretaries and Supervisors (other than those falling in the HC category) and Storekeeper Clerks.

The SA, GA and HC categories include those staff regraded in the General Grades, referred to in Part C of the Appendix to A.C. Circular No. 76 of the Administrative and Clerical Staffs Whitley Council (December 1959).

Throughout the text, the terms 'Clerical Staff' and 'Clerical Grades' refer to staff both in the 'HC' and 'C' categories mentioned above; the term 'Administrative Grades' refers to staff both in the 'SA' and 'GA' categories and, unless otherwise indicated, the terms 'Designated Grades' or 'Designated Officers' refer to all three categories D.1, D.2 and D.3. Unless they are specifically referred to, our figures and calculations exclude shorthand-typists and machine operators.

There are staff who retain designated titles such as Deputy Group Secretary, Deputy Finance Officer and Hospital Secretary but are, in fact, paid on the salary scales applicable to the general grades (see Appendix 2.i). Throughout the survey these staff are included in the grades on which they are paid.

Abbreviations

A & C   = Administrative and Clerical staff as defined above
D or D.O. = Designated Officers
SA   = Senior Administrative grade as defined above
GA   = General   „   „   „   „   „
HC   = Higher Clerical   „   „   „   „
C   = Clerical   „   „   „   „   „
NHS   = National Health Service

Summary

In making the following summary of the information contained in this report, we have excluded the assumptions and calculations on which our findings are based.

Conclusions based solely on the condensed and unqualified data which this summary contains could, therefore, be misleading. Nevertheless we felt that a summary would be a useful part of our report and that those who wished to draw conclusions from it would refer to the succeeding chapters before doing so.

---

1. At the 31st December 1960 there were 32,211 full-time administrative and clerical staff in the hospital service (England and Wales); 11,279 (35%) men, 20,932 (65%) women; 5,712 (17·7%) in the designated and administrative grades and 26,499 (82.3%) in the clerical and other grades. Only 1·65% of female staff are in the designated and administrative grades. For details of these figures see Appendix 2.ii.

Age Structures (Chapters 2 and 3)

2. The existing age structures of staff are of primary importance to a consideration of recruitment, training, mobility and promotion.

3. The percentages of staff by sex in each of five ten-year age-groups are:

Age-Group	Male	Female
16	10%	29%
26–35	21%	23%
36–45	35%	26%
46–55	26%	17%
56+	8%	5%

4. Compared with figures taken from the Census Report the male age structure shows deficiencies in staff under age 31 ($-10·8\%$) and over age 55 ($-12·3\%$) and disproportionately large numbers between ages 31 and 55 (excess = 23·1%).

5. Three factors have had an over-riding influence on the age structures. These are:—

(a) The exceptionally large proportion of existing staff who have entered the hospital service since 1945, i.e.,

Males   71·3%
Females 88·1%

(There may be a substantial element of labour turnover in the latter figure.)

(b) The high age-level at entry of the post-1945 entrants. In the last three quinquennia (1945–59 inclusive) 42%, 37% and 34% of male entrants have been over age 32 on entry.

(c) Insufficient recruitment of young men since 1939. In the last three quinquennia (1945–59) only 14%, 22% and 36% of male entrants have been under age 23 on entry. The pre-war average was 81%. For 1960 the proportion was 48%.

Recruitment Needs (*Chapter 4*)

6. Given the existing establishments and assuming that the administrative and clerical staff were evenly distributed over the age structure, the annual recruitment needs to replace staff in the designated and administrative grades and male clerical grades on retirement would be about 258. To this figure should be added an allowance for wastage.

7. Because of the character of the age structure less than this number will be needed for the next ten years and more than this during the period 1971–90. If hospital authorities do no more and no less in each period than replace staff retiring in each period, this would probably lead to a repetition of the existing unbalanced age structure.

8. A planned recruitment policy could reduce the irregularities of the age structure during the next ten years.

Mobility (*Chapter 5*)

9. The present position is:—

20% of all male staff are not willing to move;

80% are prepared to move;

    half of these are willing to go anywhere,

    half put geographic limitations on their willingness to move;

62% have attempted to move since 1948;

30% have succeeded in moving since 1948.

10. Mobility is affected by the relatively high age-level of staff including those in "junior" grades where movement would normally be greatest. The high age-level means a high proportion of married men, and married men with children. This is so even in the junior grades. For example, over 90% of GA staff are married. Nearly all of them (82%) have children; 74% of the children are of school age.

11. Major factors affecting male staff mobility are:— Housing; insufficient financial incentive; children's schooling; lack of removal allowance; dependent relatives (other than wife and children).

12. 44% of male staff have wives engaged in full or part-time employment. This may also affect mobility. There are staff who themselves have some form of remunerative activity outside the hospital service or are engaged with their wives in a joint enterprise.

Education and Training (Chapter 6)

13. The general educational background of staff is:—

	Males %	Females %
University	3	1
Grammar/Public School	60	50
Technical/Secondary Modern	19	30
Elementary	15	9
Private	3	10

14. General educational attainments of males (by examinations):—

	Designated %	Administrative %	Clerical %
At least GCE 'O' level with 5 subjects or equivalent	68	55	33
GCE 'O' level with less than 5 subjects or equivalent	9	14	23
Nil	23	31	44

15. The proportions of male staff professionally qualified or studying are:—

	%
Designated officers	89
Administrative grades	58
Clerical grades	22

16. That such a high percentage of staff in the administrative and clerical grades are not even studying for professional qualifications (42% and 78% respectively) is probably attributable to their lack of the necessary minimal general educational requirements (see para. 14 above).

17. 23% of male staff have attended residential courses provided by or associated with the hospital service and 7% have participated in some kind of training scheme. 83% have taken University, Commercial College or Correspondence Courses since commencing their working career.

18. The general educational attainments of female staff are lower than those of the men; only 5% are professionally qualified or studying; less than 6% have participated in hospital courses or training schemes.

Career Prospects (Chapter 7)

19. Of the many factors affecting a person's promotion prospects (e.g. ability, personality, health, education, training, willingness and ability to move) those outside his own control include:—

19(*a*). *Sex.* In the past the hospital service has offered very limited prospects as a career for women. Only 345, i.e. 1·5% of the total of 20,932 women, are in the GA grade or above. In a total of 1,813 Designated Officers no more than 18, i.e. ·09%, are women.

19(*b*). *Special developments leading to an increase or decrease in establishments.* These do have an effect on promotion prospects of staff as a whole, but it is not easy to estimate this precisely.

19(*c*). *Grading Structure.* It will be apparent that however many able and otherwise qualified staff there may be at, say, the penultimate level of promotion their chances of further advancement are strictly limited by the number of jobs at the top. Similar considerations apply at every level in the staff structure.

19(*d*). *Age.* It is only in the clerical grades that salaries are on a wage-for-age basis. But at all levels, age (especially if it carries with it appropriate experience) enters into considerations affecting appointment or promotion. Thus promotion prospects may be improved or lessened for staff at particular age levels according to the character of the age structure and its relationship in shape and time to the salary or grading structure.

19(*e*). *Promotion Ages.* There is a particular aspect of the effect of age on promotion prospects which we find is not widely understood in the hospital service. We refer to the median of the ages at which hospital authorities have hitherto promoted staff from one grade to another. We call these 'promotion ages'.

20. The relationship of the grading structure to promotion ages and the effect of this relationship on the staff's promotion prospects is a difficult question. This is dealt with on pages 66 to 73.

21. Past promotion ages to the existing grades are shown in column (a) below. It has been suggested to us that these should be as shown in column (b).

	(a)	(b)
To junior Designated grades	38	38
To the SA grade	37	30
To the GA grade	34	25
To the HC grade	31	23
Median age at entry to the Clerical grade	24	20 or less

22. With the promotion ages shown in (b) then the promotion prospects of an annual intake of 258 (see para. 6) would be:—

%
67 (26) would become Designated Officers
18 (7) would go no higher than the SA grade
58 (22) would go no higher than the GA grade
72 (28) would go no higher than the HC grade
43 (17) would remain on the Clerical grade

23. Of the 67 reaching the designated grades,
    37 would be in General Management;
    20 in Finance;
    9 in Supplies and
    1 other.

Chapter 1 Scope and Content of the Survey

This is a report on a survey we have made of the hospital administrative and clerical staff in the area of four Regional Hospital Boards —Liverpool, North-East Metropolitan, Sheffield and the South Western. The area, size, population and other details of the regions are given in the tables shown in Appendix 2. We chose these regions as being reasonably representative of the regions in England and Wales as a whole. The North-East Metropolitan Region is predominantly urban (59% of the population of the region live in the Greater London area); the South Western Region is geographically the largest region in England and is principally rural; Sheffield is partly rural and partly industrial; Liverpool is geographically the smallest region in the country and has the highest population density. In terms of administrative and clerical staff these regions employ some 27% of the total of such staff employed in the hospital service of England and Wales as a whole; 122 of the 125 hospital authorities in the four regions[1] co-operated in the survey which was made during the period July 1960 to September 1961; our statistics relate to the position at that time. Such changes as have occurred since then (e.g. a cost of living adjustment in salaries made in April 1961; the amalgamation of two of the hospital groups in the South Western Region) do not substantially affect our findings.

Our main interest was in the staff who are seeking to make a career in either the administrative or clerical work associated with hospital management. We use the term 'hospital management' in its widest sense to include the administrative and clerical work in Regional Boards, Boards of Governors, Management Committees and individual hospitals.

Some preliminary enquiries revealed that very little of the information we needed was readily available in the records of the hospital authorities themselves. To those unfamiliar with the history and traditions of the hospital service this may seem strange; they might think that, at least since nationalization in 1948 when the hospitals were brought together in groups subject to some measure of regional and central control,[2] there would be, either nationally or regionally, a considerable amount of data about such things as the numbers, ages, sex, educational background, training and job history of the staff engaged in this important section of a national service which in total employs 431,000 people[3] and costs the community £415 million per annum.[4]

1

The reason that such information is not readily available in the hands of the Ministry of Health or even of Regional Boards is that the Service is designed to give a considerable measure of autonomy in staffing matters not only to the Boards but also to the 378 Hospital Management Committees.[5] Many Group Secretaries (i.e. the chief administrative officers of the Management Committees) might say that there is not much local autonomy; it is, however, a fact that in the matter of administrative and clerical staff recruitment and training, and hence the responsibility for staff records, hospital authorities until recently have been largely left to their own devices.

In 1956 the Ministry of Health initiated a 'National Training Scheme' for hospital administrators,[6] but this has a limited intake of twenty-four (originally only sixteen) recruits a year. At the same time the hospital authorities were invited to make their own arrangements for the in-service training of existing staff. More recently Regional Staff Advisory Committees have been established who have a co-ordinating function in this connection, and during the present year (1962) the Ministry have introduced a 'Regional Training Scheme'[7] which is broadly similar to the National Training Scheme. But none of these developments has hitherto made any marked encroachment upon the recruiting and appointing autonomy of the local group committees. For all that the hospital service is a 'national' service, it is not staffed by a *corps* of administrative staff in the way that many other public and private large-scale organizations are.

In 1957 Sir Noel Hall, in his *Report on the Grading Structure of Administrative and Clerical Staff in the Hospital Service*, referred to the 'little worlds' and 'fragmentation' of the administrative and clerical staff of the hospital service.[8] As an aid to a consideration of the recruitment and training needs of the Service he recommended the compilation of regional registers which should contain 'records of fact', such as details of age, length of service, posts held, professional and other qualifications, but 'no routine reports by senior officers upon their juniors'.[9]

Regions have been cautious in following Noel Hall's recommendations. Some have not acted at all and even those who have started a register have not usually gone beyond inviting staff to submit their particulars voluntarily. As a result no region has information for all the administrative and clerical staff in its area beyond the absolute numbers in each grade required by the Ministry in their annual returns SH6 and SH7. Not even such important details as the division between

2

men and women and their ages and length of service are known for all administrative and clerical staff to any one Regional Staff Advisory Committee.[10]

Of the four regions in our survey the Sheffield Regional Staff Advisory Committee had the largest amount of information readily available but, excellent though it was, it did not refer to clerical staff; it did not cover all the staff in the higher grades; nor did it provide answers to all the questions which we wanted to ask. Because of the lack of the information we wanted in any existing records, we decided to make a direct approach to each member of the full-time staff (other than typists and machine operators) with the letter and form of questionnaire shown in Appendix 1; 6,444 forms were sent out and 3,082 (i.e. 48%) were returned. This is about twice the customary response to a postal enquiry.[11]

For the following reasons the sample is more significant than this response seems to indicate. We have already said that our main interest was in 'career staff' and at the outset of our enquiry we contemplated confining ourselves to the General Administrative grade and above.[12] But inevitably we were drawn into including the Higher Clerical grade because it is from this grade that the majority of General Administrative staff are at present recruited and this led to our including also the Clerical grade because this grade supplies the candidates for many Higher Clerical appointments. In including the Clerical and Higher Clerical grades we realized that we should be taking in a substantial number of 'non-career' staff with whom we were only marginally

Table 1 *Summary of Total of Staff, by Grades and Sex in the Four Regions and the Number and Percentage of the Response to the Questionnaire*

Grade	Total			Response			%		
	M	F	M+F	M	F	M+F	M	F	M+F
Designated . . .	472	5	477	330	4	334	70	80	70
Administrative . .	955	87	1,042	629	53	682	66	61	65
Clerical	1,479	3,446	4,925	767	1,299	2,066	52	38	42
			6,444			3,082			48

3

concerned. Many of these non-career staff excluded themselves, however, because it was the clerical staff and in particular female clerical staff who did not respond as well as other grades to our questionnaire. Table 1 gives a summary of the numbers and proportions of staff who responded. Appendix 2(iv) gives full details of the number and percentage of staff in each of the four regions by grade and sex and the percentage response from each section.

As a percentage of the equivalent staff in England and Wales the response was:

				%
Designated Grades	.	.	.	18·3
Administrative Grades	.	.	.	17·5
Clerical Grades:	Men	.	.	13·0
	Women.	.		9·4

Because of the undertaking we had given in our letter and questionnaire about the 'strictly confidential' character of the survey we made no attempt to identify individual members of staff among either those who had responded or those who had not. From the enquiries we made of Group Secretaries as to which kind of clerical staff had not participated in the enquiry we learned that these seemed to be, for the most part, the young female and the elderly male clerks. The majority of such staff have limited career interests, if any at all. Thus our sample is a sizeable proportion and represents a fair cross-section of those men and women for whom hospital administration and clerical work present career prospects.* Nevertheless, as we shall see, even within the sample there are two substantial groups who are 'non-career' or 'limited career' staff. These distinctions are of importance for any personnel policy concerned with recruitment and training needs and staff promotion prospects. Equally important for such a personnel policy are the existing age structures of the staff.

Before we consider the age structures and comment upon them we

* The representative character of our sample is borne out by figures which have become available only within a short time of going to press (October 1962). In the last few months the Ministry of Health have commenced an enquiry. This relates only to the designated and administrative grades but has the advantage of including all staff in those grades. With one exception all of the 122 co-operating authorities in our four regions have sent us a copy of the return they made to the Ministry. A comparison of the statistics in these returns shows a close correlation with the data contained in this report. An example of the correlation is given in the footnote on page 11.

4

want to describe briefly how we collected and dealt with the information contained in this survey.

All of the administrative and clerical staff with whom we were concerned in the four regions personally received a copy of our letter and questionnaire (Appendix 1) and a reply-paid envelope. The process of collecting the replies occupied the period October 1960 to March 1961. The information we obtained was coded and transferred to punched cards. Analyses and Appendices such as those contained in this report were prepared for each of the four regions. The statistics given in the accompanying Appendices are a combination of the four separate sets.

A set of the statistics relating to their region and also a set of the combined statistics and a copy of the draft of our report were sent for comment to the secretaries of each of the four Regional Boards and to other senior administrators in the regions. We also invited a number of people closely associated with the hospital service to read the draft of our report and comment upon it.

At the same time as our survey another was made of the hospital administrative and clerical staff in Wales by the Welsh Hospital Board. By arrangement with us, the Board used a questionnaire form identical to ours and conducted their enquiries along similar lines. They were assisted in this by Miss Anne Crichton, of the University College of South Wales and Monmouthshire.

We welcomed this action of the Welsh Hospital Board and the co-operation we received from Mr. John Phillips, the Board's Training Officer, because, although they conducted their enquiry with the same form and along similar lines to ours, the analysis and interpretation of the information they received were in their hands or Miss Crichton's. Since the analysis and interpretation of data of the kind contained in the completed questionnaires cannot be wholly objective, we were glad to have the results of the Welsh survey for comparison with our own.

There are no major differences between the pattern revealed by their data and ours. We have not, however, commented upon the Welsh statistics because these are the subject of an independent report.[13]

Chapter 2   Age Structures

A proper understanding of the existing age structures of the hospital administrative and clerical staff is of primary importance to much of what follows in other chapters of our report. We shall therefore deal with this in some detail.

Male Age Structure

The ages of the men in the survey group are given in Appendix 3. The number and proportion of staff in each of the five-year age-groups from 16 to 65 are given in Table 2.

Table 2 *Number and Percentage of Male Administrative and Clerical Staff in the Survey Group. Five-year Age-groups by Grades*

Index	Grade of staff	Age-groups (in years)										Age not known	Total
		16–	21–	26–	31–	36–	41–	46–	51–	56–	61–		
Number of Staff	Designated .				9	45	68	99	72	27	10		330
	Senior Admin.			7	16	47	58	37	17	9	5		196
	General Admin.		3	41	58	120	82	63	37	19	9	1	433
	Higher Clerical	3	44	74	87	78	65	44	29	13	7		444
	Clerical . .	97	34	28	34	27	22	22	25	12	22		323
	Total . . .	100	81	150	204	317	295	265	180	80	53	1	1,726
% of Total	Designated .				0·5	2·6	3·9	5·7	4·2	1·5	0·6		19·0
	Senior Admin.			0·4	0·9	2·7	3·4	2·1	1·0	0·5	0·3		11·3
	General Admin.		0·2	2·4	3·4	7·0	4·8	3·6	2·1	1·1	0·5		25·1
	Higher Clerical	0·2	2·5	4·3	5·0	4·5	3·8	2·6	1·7	0·8	0·4		25·8
	Clerical . .	5·6	2·0	1·6	2·0	1·6	1·3	1·3	1·4	0·7	1·3		18·8
	Total . . .	5·8	4·7	8·7	11·8	18·4	17·2	15·3	10·4	4·6	3·1		100
% in each 10-yr age-group		10·5		20·5		35·6		25·7		7·7			100

The percentages shown in Table 2 give the age-grade patterns shown in Figure 1.

In a labour force with an even age structure, for all grades combined there would be approximately 10% of the staff in each five-year age-grouping.

Compared with a 10% 'norm' the extent of the imbalance of the male age structure of hospital administrative and clerical staff is shown in Table 3.

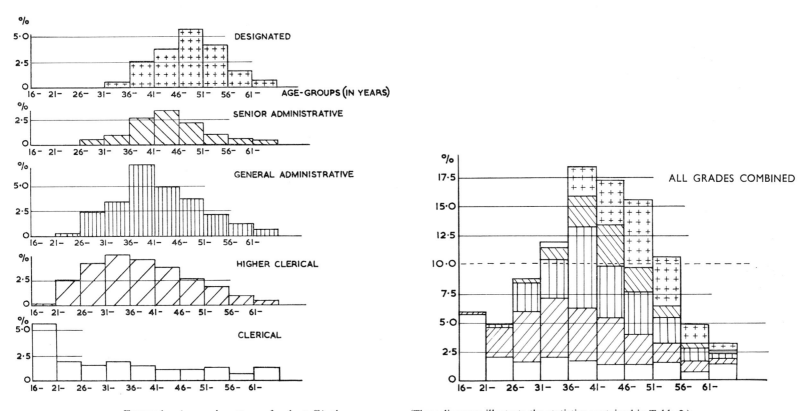

FIGURE 1 *Age-grade patterns of male staff in the survey group.* (These diagrams illustrate the statistics contained in Table 2.)

Table 3 *Comparison of Percentage of Staff in each Five-year Age-group with a 10% Norm*

Age-group (Years)	% of staff	More (+) or Less (−) than 10%		Aggregates
		+	−	
16 – 20	5·8		4·2	⎫
21 – 25	4·7		5·3	⎬ − 10·8
26 – 30	8·7		1·3	⎭
31 – 35	11·8	1·8		⎫
36 – 40	18·4	8·4 ⎫		⎪
41 – 45	17·2	7·2 ⎬ 20·9		⎬ + 23·1
46 – 50	15·3	5·3 ⎪		⎪
51 – 55	10·4	0·4 ⎭		⎭
56 – 60	4·6		5·4	⎫ − 12·3
61 +	3·1		6·9	⎭

Assuming the desirability of a more or less even age structure, there is a 'deficiency' of staff in the Service of about 11% and 12% in the age categories under 31 and 56–65 respectively and an 'excess' of staff of some 23% between ages 31 and 55.

An unbalanced age structure is not peculiar to the hospital service. For comparison, Figure 2 shows graphs of the male age structure for the hospital service, the civil service and two of the 'Big Five' banks.

In Chapter 3 we shall be discussing why the age structure of the male administrative and clerical staff of the hospital service should be approximately even.

It is, of course, only the age structure for such staff *as a whole* which could be approximately even and only then if the total number of staff is a large one, as it is in the labour forces illustrated in Figure 2.

The percentages of the staff in each age-group will clearly be different for the various grades of staff within the total. For all grades combined, however, it is desirable that there should be about the same proportion of staff in each age-group over the whole working span.

A striking feature of the male age structure of the administrative and clerical staff in the hospital service is the 'persistence' of the peak between ages 31 and 55. Whereas the age structure of some organiza-

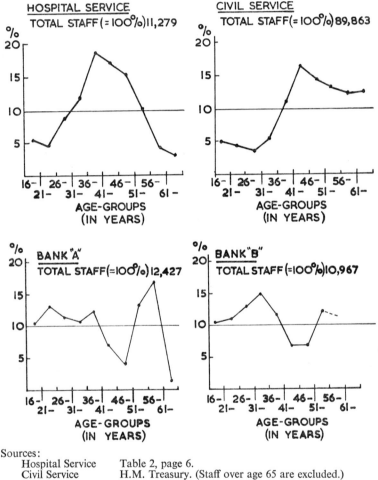

FIGURE 2 *Male administrative and clerical staff in five-year age-groups. A comparison of the hospital service with the civil service and two banks*

Sources:
Hospital Service   Table 2, page 6.
Civil Service   H.M. Treasury. (Staff over age 65 are excluded.)
Bank 'A'   Private communication.
Bank 'B'   Private communication.

The data relating to the civil service and the banks are for 1962. Those for the hospital service are for the date of our survey, 1960–61.

tions tends to flatten out over ten-year age-groupings, this is not so in the hospital service. For instance, the figure for Bank 'A' drawn on the basis of ten-year age-groups 16–, 26–, 36–, etc., is shown in Figure 3 (*a*); the hospital male age structure on the same basis—Figure 3 (*b*) —remains excessive between ages 31 and 55.

A similar position is revealed if the hospital age structure is compared with data available in the census reports. The 1951 Census[14] (the latest Census figures available at the time of writing) gives statistics in ten-year age-groupings relating to the total employed male population

FIGURE 3 *Male administrative and clerical staff in ten-year age groups. A comparison of the hospital service with Bank 'A'*

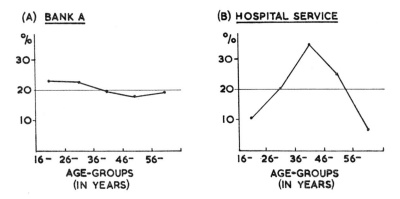

Sources: as for Figure 2.

and employed males being 'Civil Service Executive and Higher Clerical Officers' and 'Clerks'. These are compared with the hospital service in Figure 4.

Just as there would be approximately 10% of the staff in each five-year age-group given an even age structure so, all other things being equal, we should expect there to be about 20% of the male labour force in each ten-year age-grouping. Figures 3 and 4 show that for the employed male population as a whole and for workers in some comparable forms of employment this is approximately so. But in the hospital service the age structure is grossly out of balance. If the

9

FIGURE 4 *Proportion of employed males (administrative and clerical staff) in ten-year age-groups*

% = % of men in each of the ten-year age-groups shown on horizontal axis

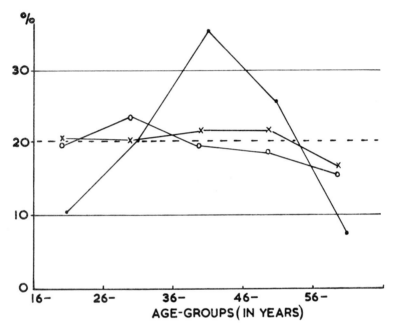

KEY:

———————· = Male (administrative and clerical) staff of Hospital Service.

o————o = Employed males being 'Civil Service Executive and Higher Clerical Officers' and 'Clerks'

x————x = Total employed male population.

Sources: Hospital Service—Table 2, page 6.

Other figures—Part 1 1951 Census Report Table II.3.

10

hospital service age structure included all male staff it is possible that the peak would be slightly less than that shown in Figure 4, because the indications are that among the male staff who did not respond to the questionnaire there is a higher proportion of elderly men than among the male staff included in the survey (see page 4). But the characteristics of the male age structure for the South Western Region (see Figure 5, page 12), in which there was a high response from male staff, suggests that the inclusion of a greater number of male staff would not greatly affect the outlines of the curves shown in these Figures.*

There are some differences in the male age structure of the four regions we surveyed. These are shown in Figure 5.

On the face of it the region nearest to the 20% norm is Liverpool and the one furthest from it (except in the higher age-groups) is the NE Metropolitan. The differences between these two regions in the lower age-groups are possibly attributable to the greater opportunities for young men at more attractive rates of pay in the metropolitan area and to the fact that, in a total of forty-four male clerical staff in the Liverpool survey group, nearly half are at ages 17, 18 and 19—an exceptional state of affairs which results in part from the activities of

---

* Since this was written we have had the benefit of comparing our figures with those that result from an enquiry at present being made by the Ministry of Health. Their figures relate only to designated and administrative grades. A comparison between our age structure for these grades based on the *survey sample* shows the following close similarity (except in age-group 36–40) with the age structure drawn from the Ministry's data which covers *all* staff in those grades.

————— = Survey sample

- - - - - - = Ministry enquiry

Designated and administrative grades (both sexes).

Proportion of staff in five-year age-groups.

Sources:

(a) Statistics contained in this Survey

(b) Statistics contained in Ministry of Health forms SBH.100.

N.B. Our statistics relate to 1960–61. Ministry of Health statistics relate to 1962.

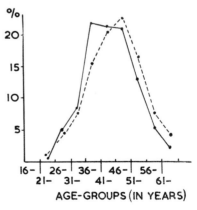

AGE-GROUPS (IN YEARS)

FIGURE 5 *Proportion of male (administrative and clerical) staff in ten-year age-groups. The four regions shown separately*

% = % of staff in each of the ten-year age-groups shown on the horizontal axis

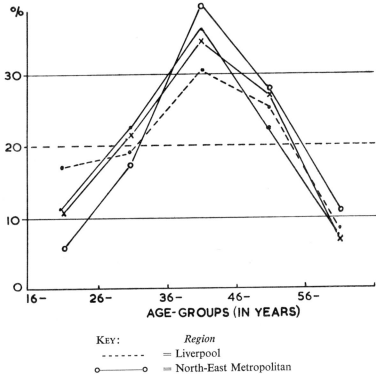

KEY: *Region*
- - - - - -   = Liverpool
o———o   = North-East Metropolitan
._____.   = Sheffield
x———x   = South Western

one Management Committee who have been particularly successful in recruiting grammar school leavers in recent years.

Above age 35 the NE Metropolitan Region has a consistently higher proportion of men in all grades than have the other regions. There appears to be a markedly lower proportion of men between 41 and 45 in the Liverpool Region (12·2%) compared with the other three (NE Metropolitan 21·6%, Sheffield 15·4% and South Western 16·8%). The age structure of all four regions is, however, broadly similar, i.e. each contributes its share to the pattern shown in Figure 4. We think that it is not unreasonable to assume that Figure 4 gives a fair indication of the age structure of the male administrative and clerical staff of England and Wales as a whole.

Female Age Structure

The ages of the women in the survey group are given in Appendix 4.

The number of staff in each five-year age-group from 16 to 65 is shown in Table 4.

Table 4 *Number and Percentage of Female Administrative and Clerical Staff in the Survey Group. Five-year Age-groups by Grades*

Index	Grade of Staff	16–	21–	26–	31–	36–	41–	46–	51–	56–	61–	Age not known	Total
Number of Staff	Designated .						1	2		1			4
	Senior Admin.												6
	General Admin.			3	4	11	8	11	7	2	1		47
	Higher Clerical		18	29	42	66	52	51	28	21	2	1	310
	Clerical . .	177	201	128	102	128	89	68	58	29	8	1	989
	Total . .	177	219	160	148	206	151	136	93	53	11	2	1,356
	% of Total	13·1	16·2	11·8	10·9	15·2	11·1	10·0	6·8	3·9	0·8	0·1	100
	% in each ten-year age-group .	29·3		22·7		26·3		16·8		4·7		0·1	

The curve of the percentage in each ten-year age-group compared with that of the total employed female population and employed women being 'Clerks, Typists, etc.' (Part 1, 1951 Census Report, Table 11.3) is plotted in Figure 6.

The curves in Figure 6 reflect the effect of marriage on the female

13

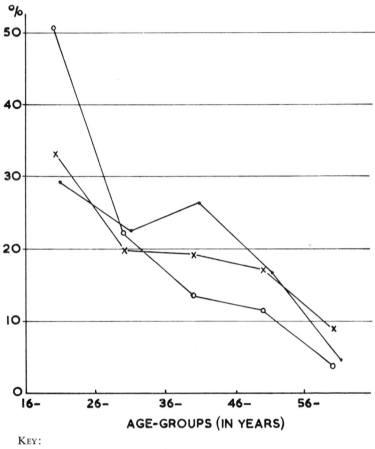

FIGURE 6 *Proportion of employed women in ten-year age groups*
% = % of women in each of the ten-year age-groups shown on horizontal axis

AGE-GROUPS (IN YEARS)

KEY:

._____. = Female (administrative and clerical) staff of Hospital Service
o_____o = Employed females being 'Clerks, Typists, etc.'
x_____x = Total employed female population

14

FIGURE 7 *Proportion of female (administrative and clerical) staff in ten-year age-groups. Four regions shown separately*
% = % in each of the ten-year age-groups shown in the horizontal axis

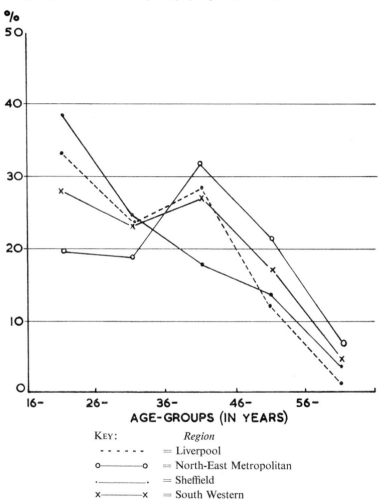

%

KEY: *Region*
- - - - - -   = Liverpool
o———o   = North-East Metropolitan
.————.   = Sheffield
x———x   = South Western

15

labour force. When comparing the curve relating to 'Clerks, Typists, etc.' with that for the hospital service there are two points to remember: the figures for the Service do not include typists and machine operators; also, as we said on page 4, many of the female clerks who did not respond to the questionnaire may be in the lower age-groups. If allowance is made for these factors, the hospital curve would probably approximate more nearly to the other two.

The comparative curves for the four regions are shown in Figure 7.

The relatively poor response (except in the South Western Region) from the large numbers of female clerical staff prevents us from drawing any reliable conclusions from the differences between the regions revealed in Figure 7.

Factors Affecting the Shape of the Age Structures

Many things influence the age structures of staff in the hospital service, just as they do in any organization; for example, they will be affected by:

(*a*) The availability of labour and the effect upon this of such things as war, national service, depression, boom.

(*b*) What command the hospital service has over the labour market —the prospects it can offer (especially in the matter of pay, promotion and interesting work) and the extent to which these are competitive or not with those in comparable jobs in other places of employment. (Pay and prospects are of particular importance at the points of entry: see page 27.)

The factors referred to in (*a*) and (*b*) may, of course, vary from one area of the country to another.

(*c*) Any exceptional expansion or contraction of the labour force.

(*d*) Labour turnover and the ages at which people leave and others are brought in to replace them.

(*e*) The personnel practices of hospital authorities, e.g. preferences for male or female labour for various kinds of work, the attitude of authorities to recruitment and the ages at which promotion takes place.

Furthermore, to be able to account fully for the shape of an age structure curve at any given date we would need to have detailed staff statistics for each year over a considerable period of time. At present information of this kind is not available in the hospital service.

Chapter 3 Comments on the Age Structure

There is, of course, nothing sacrosanct about an even age structure and the reader may wonder why we should suggest, as we do later, that one of the objectives of recruitment policy should be to attain it. It is conceivable that in some forms of employment an uneven structure is an advantage. In heavy labouring, for instance, the ideal age structure curve is probably one that is roughly dome shaped, tapering off at about 45. This presumes that with advancing years the men doing such work will have to find alternative employment within the industry or elsewhere. For administrative and clerical work, however, where such conditions and alternatives do not apply, the age structure of a male labour force should normally be more or less even with about 10% of the staff in each five-year age-group.

A grossly unbalanced age structure such as that of the male hospital administrative and clerical staff produces many undesirable consequences. We shall refer later to the difficulties it creates in connection with recruitment and its adverse effects on staff mobility and the organization of training. It almost certainly gives rise to a considerable amount of discontent among staff within the age-ranges around the peak. Their prospects of promotion are diminished by the excessive number of competitors of their own age and of co-equal attainments.

Further unfortunate results occur when the men in the peak ages reach retirement. There may then be unduly rapid promotion for a large number of young staff. This will generate still further discontent among men more senior to them in years and experience who are being passed over (as they see it) solely because of age.

Unduly rapid promotion could, indeed, be bad for the Service and for those who get it if they miss, or move too quickly through, stages that are essential parts of their development as administrators. Rapid promotion will also block promotion for a future generation of junior staff. The lower the age at which staff are appointed to senior posts the smaller the number of potential occupants. Thus there will be a falling-off in career prospects and in the offers which can be made to would-be recruits.

These conditions are aggravated if, as in the hospital service, the peak in the age structure is succeeded by a substantial deficiency of staff over a wide age-span. 'Unduly rapid promotion' may become 'leap-frogging'—the effects we have described might then be accentuated.

For these reasons, among others, we think it is advisable for the hospital service to move towards a more even distribution of administrative and clerical staff over the whole age-range of 16 to 65. This is a point to which we return in our discussion of recruitment needs (see Chapter 4).

We said at the conclusion of the last chapter that to be able to account fully for the characteristics of an age structure curve we should need to have detailed staff statistics for each year over a considerable period of time, and that this information is not available in the hospital service.

From the particulars we have collected we can, however, throw some light on several of the factors which cause the unbalanced age structures illustrated in Figures 4 and 6.

It will be seen from the tables and figures given earlier that there is an excessively large proportion of male staff in all four regions between the ages of approximately 31 and 55 (especially between 36 and 50), and it seems that women also contribute slightly to the 'excess' of staff between these ages.

Three factors appear to have had an over-riding influence on the age structures. They are:

(1) The disproportionately large number of new entrants in the years since 1945;

(2) The high age level at which they entered; this was probably not as much from choice as from the hospital authorities' needs to staff the service; recruitment at a high age-level helped to redress:

(3) The insufficient recruitment of young men during the major part of the period 1945-60.

Years of Entry into Hospital Service (Men)

Appendix 5 shows how many of the existing male staff joined the hospital service in each year from 1913 and their age at entry.

Figure 8 summarizes the number and percentage of the total of the existing men entering the Service in each five-year period from 1920 up to and including 1959. We have excluded 1960 because our data for that year are not complete.

The percentage figures for each of the four regions are given in Table 5.

18

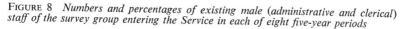

FIGURE 8 *Numbers and percentages of existing male (administrative and clerical) staff of the survey group entering the Service in each of eight five-year periods*

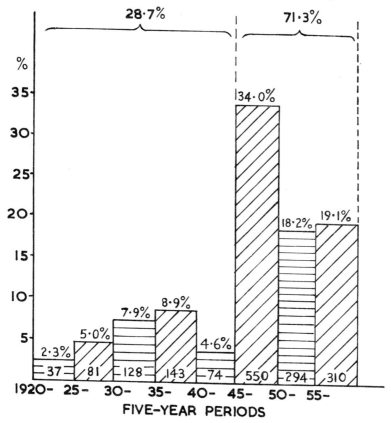

Each of the four regions will be seen to have a very large proportion of existing male staff who have joined the Service since 1945 (i.e. 71·3% for the four regions combined). The individual figures for the regions are:

Region	%
Liverpool	70·0
North-East Metropolitan . .	64·5
Sheffield	72·6
South Western	76·0

19

Table 5 *Percentage of Existing Male (Administrative and Clerical) Staff of the Survey Group entering the Service in each of eight Five-year Periods. The four Regions Shown Separately*

Five-year period	Liverpool		North-East Metropolitan		Sheffield		South Western		Four regions	
	No.	% of total	No.	% of total	No.	% of total	No.	% of total	No.	% of total
1920–	5	2·3	12	2·8	10	2·7	10	1·7	37	2·3 ⎫
1925–	11	5·0	30	7·1	14	3·8	26	4·3	81	5·0 ⎪
1930–	21	9·6	36	8·5	32	8·6	39	6·5	128	7·9 ⎬ 28·7
1935–	16	7·3	48	11·4	34	9·1	45	7·4	143	8·9 ⎪
1940–	13	5·9	24	5·7	12	3·2	25	4·1	74	4·6 ⎭
1945–	60	27·4	140	33·3	129	34·7	221	36·7	550	34·0 ⎫
1950–	38	17·2	58	13·7	78	21·0	120	19·9	294	18·2 ⎬ 71·3
1955–	56	25·4	74	17·5	63	16·9	117	19·4	310	19·1 ⎭
Total	220	100	422	100	372	100	603	100	1,617	100
Pre-1920	2		2				2		6	
1960 (part-year)	15		16		18		43		92(a)	
Unknown	1		5				5		11	
	238		445		390		653		1,726	

(a) For analysis of this number see page 25.

Lest it be thought that these high percentages can be attributed to the inclusion of 'transferred officers' among staff who 'have joined the Service since 1945', we would point out the comprehensiveness of our definition of 'hospital service' (see page xx). Staff who before nationalization were employed in the hospitals section of a public health department—though not necessarily at a hospital—have been counted as having joined the hospital service in the year of their appointment to the public health service. On the other hand, there are some staff formerly employed in, for example, a Treasurer's or Public Works department of local government, but not directly associated with hospital work, whose date of joining the hospital service has been taken to be the year in which they entered the employment of a hospital authority created by the National Health Service Act, 1946. If anything, the figures shown in Table 5 probably understate slightly the percentages of staff entering the hospital service since 1945.

Years of Entry into the Hospital Service (Women)

The female age structure is influenced by such factors as the large number of short-stay staff and marriage and child-bearing.

The high proportion of short-stay female staff probably accounts for the substantial number of entrants in the last few years, as shown in Appendix 6, which states how many of the existing women joined the hospital service in each year from 1918 and their ages at entry. The relatively higher proportions of female entrants since 1940 possibly also reflects the deficiencies in the recruitment of young men since that date.

These numbers and the percentage of the total of the existing women entering the service in each five-year period from 1920 up to and including 1959 are summarized in Table 6. As with male staff we have excluded 1960 because our data for that year are incomplete.

The numbers and percentages for the South Western Region are given separately because of the larger percentage response in that region from the female clerical staff. It will be seen, however, that the proportions of staff recruited in each period for the four regions taken together are approximately the same.

Table 6 *Percentage of Existing Female (Administrative and Clerical) Staff of the Survey Group entering the Service in each of eight Five-year Periods*

The four Regions taken together and South Western Region

Five-year Period	Four regions		South Western Region	
	Number	*% of Total*	*Number*	*% of Total*
1920–24	4	0·3	2	0·4
1925–29	14	1·2	3	0·6
1930–34	18	1·5	7	1·3
1935–39	24	2·1	13	2·5
1940–44	80	6·8	33	6·4
1945–49	238	20·4	108	20·8
1950–54	293	25·0	133	25·6
1955–59	500	42·7	220	42·4
Total	1,171	100	519	100
Pre-1920	2		1	
1960 (part-year)	158 (*a*)		58	
Unknown	25		9	
Gross Total	1,356		587	

(*a*) For analysis of this number see page 25.

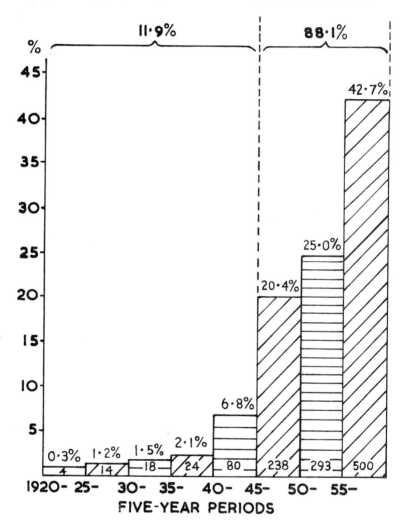

Figure 9, which relates to female staff, is given for comparison with Figure 8 (male staff).

Ages at Entry (Men)

The entry of 71·3% of the existing male staff (see Figure 8) in a comparatively short period, i.e. in the years 1945–59, has had a marked effect upon the age structure because the majority of these were recruited at a high age level. This is shown in Table 7—a summary of the ages at entry for each five-year age-group given in Appendix 5.

Table 7 *Age at Entry of Existing Male (Administrative and Clerical) Staff in the Survey Group*

(a)	(b)	(c)	(d)			
			% of entrants at (b) in age groups:			
Years of Entry	No. of Entrants	% of Total (see Fig. 6)	14–	20–	26–	32 and above
1920–24	37	2·3 ⎫	76	21	3	
1925–29	81	5·0 ⎪	64	29	7	
1930–34	128	7·9 ⎬ 28·7	70	20	8	2
1935–39	143	8·9 ⎪	65	19	10	6
1940–44	74	4·6 ⎭	60	7	12	21
1945–49	550	34·0 ⎫	6	20	32	42
1950–54	294	18·2 ⎬ 71·3	9	29	25	37
1955–59	310	19·1 ⎭	22	28	16	34
Total	1,617					
Pre-1920	6					
1960 (part-year)	92(e)					
Unknown	11					
Gross Total	1,726					

(d) See comments immediately preceding Table 8.
(e) For analysis of this number see page 25.

Of the 844, i.e. 550 + 294, recruited in the years 1945–54 (*N.B.* this is 52·2% of the existing male labour force in the survey group) their ages at recruitment were:

   58 (7%) at 14–
194 (23%) at 20–
248 (29%) at 26–⎫
167 (20%) at 32–⎭ 415 (49%) between 26 and 37
114 (14%) at 38–
  62 (7%) at 44–
    1   unknown

The 415 men who entered at ages between 26 and 37 in 1945–54 were in 1960 within the age range 32 to 52. For the most part it is these that account for the peak of the age structure between these ages. From Table 7 and Appendix 5 it will be seen that there has been an increase in recruitment at the lower age levels in the last five-year period and in 1960 (part year), but there is still a substantial proportion being recruited over age 25.

Ages at Entry (Women)

The ages at entry of existing female staff in the survey group in each five-year period is shown in Appendix 6. This is summarized in Table 8.

In considering these figures and those contained in Table 7, the reader will recognize that they relate solely to *existing* staff. In the absence of adequate and readily available staff records for the past

Table 8 *Age at Entry of Existing Female (Administrative and Clerical) Staff in the Survey Group*

(a)	(b)	(c)	(d)			
			% of entrants at (b) in age groups:			
Years of Entry	No. of Entrants	% of Total	14–	20–	26–	32 and above
1920–24	4	0·3	100			
1925–29	14	1·2	93	7		
1930–34	18	1·5	67	28		5
1935–39	24	2·1	29	25	21	25
1940–44	80	6·8	30	19	16	35
1945–49	238	20·4	16	20	23	41
1950–54	293	25·0	28	18	17	37
1955–59	500	42·7	34	21	11	34
Total	1,171					
Pre-1920	2					
1960 (part-year)	158(e)					
Unknown	25					
Gross Total	1,356					

(e) For analysis of this number see page 25.

we cannot give information about staff who have left. This obviously affects the details contained in these tables for the earlier periods and could conceivably affect the later periods as well. If, for instance, there had been a large entry of young men aged 14–19 in the period 1945–54 who had left the Service before the date of our survey, the percentages for this period given in the first column of section (*d*) in Table 7 would probably be higher. Similarly, any person who was aged 32 or more upon entry at a date prior to 1927 and who retired at 65 would not be shown in the first two lines of the fourth column of section (*d*) of these tables.

The effects on our figures of the fact that they relate solely to existing staff are likely to have a particular bearing on the data relating to female staff, among whom we believe there is a high proportion of short-stay staff.

Nevertheless, the figures, and more especially those relating to the male staff, do give an indication of what has been happening over the past twenty-five years or so, i.e. a high proportion of youthful entrants before the war; a fall in this proportion in the war years, particularly of entrants in the 20–25 age-group; a substantial recruitment since 1945 of both men and women in age-groups over 25; some recovery in the proportion of young male entrants in the last quinquennium (1955–59), but still a high percentage of recruits of both sexes over age 25 and approximately one-third of all entrants up to 1959 still over age 32.

We excluded the year 1960 from the tables relating to ages at entry because our survey commenced before the end of that year and does not therefore include staff who joined after the issue of the questionnaire. Our figures for the incomplete year are, however, of some interest and are given in Table 9.

Table 9 *Number and Age at Entry of New Entrants in the Survey Group during* 1960 (*Part-year*)

(*a*)	(*b*)	(*c*)			
	No. of Entrants	% *of entrants at* (b) *in age-groups:*			
		14–	20–	26–	32 *and above*
Males . .	92	41	16	12	31
Females .	158	40	28	12	20

The figures for men show a marked improvement in the proportion of entrants in the 14–19 age-group, but a continuing proportion of nearly one-third are over age 32. There may sometimes be good reasons for the recruitment of staff above this age; but our view is that for as long as the age structure is grossly out of balance the appointment of men from outside the Service at ages over 30 should be limited and should in no foreseeable circumstances be as much as one-third of the total number of new entrants.

Insufficient Recruitment of Young Men

There are undoubtedly many reasons why the hospital service was seemingly unable to recruit an adequate number of young men in the years 1945–49. Almost certainly one reason was the rates of pay which hospital authorities could offer, especially at the conventional points of entry, i.e. ages 16, 18 and 21 or (at the time of National Service) 23. These rates were lower relative to comparable forms of employment. Salaries have been raised slightly for hospital administrative and clerical staff since the date of our survey, but so they have in the services with which we have made comparisons. When, in 1960, we made enquiries about the basic rates paid to clerical staff in the Civil Service, Local Government and Bank 'A' the conditions were as indicated in Figure 10. It should be borne in mind, however, that notwithstanding their relatively higher rates of pay, these services were also experiencing difficulty in recruiting young men (see pages 28–29).

We are not saying that Figure 10 does more than point to a condition under which hospital authorities were partially handicapped in their recruitment activities. We did not pursue our enquiry into relative salary rates very far, for the difficulty of comparing responsibilities of staff in one service with another makes such comparisons of limited value. The situation revealed by Figure 10 seems to suggest, however, that if hospital authorities were not particularly successful in recruiting young men from 1945 to 1959 this was not entirely because of deficiencies in their recruitment activities. In 1956, Clegg and Chester observed that 'All sections of health service staff apart from Ancillary Staff and Nurses have fallen behind the rise in the cost of living and the rise in average wage rates'[15] and further, 'Health Service administrators are paid less than most administrators'.[16] Salary rates have an obvious bearing upon an employer's recruitment potential.

In their evidence before the Royal Commission on the Civil Service

FIGURE 10 *Salary scales (1960) for clerical grade staff in the hospital service and for equivalent staff in comparable forms of employment* (Provincial rates).

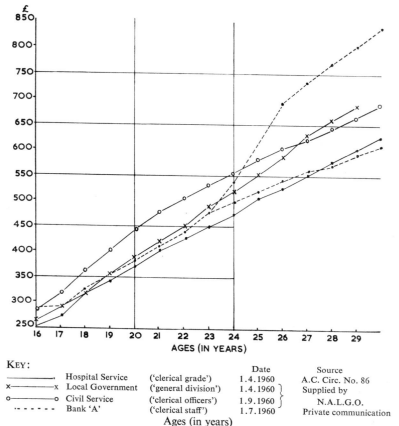

KEY:

			Date	Source
————•	Hospital Service	('clerical grade')	1.4.1960	A.C. Circ. No. 86
x————x	Local Government	('general division')	1.4.1960 ⎫	Supplied by
o————o	Civil Service	('clerical officers')	1.9.1960 ⎬	N.A.L.G.O.
•-------	Bank 'A'	('clerical staff')	1.7.1960 ⎭	Private communication

Ages (in years)

There are 'bars' at ages 24 (Local Govt.) and 29 (Civil Service). Staff in the hospital service engaged on 'routine' duties may not go beyond £555 p.a.

At each age the characteristics for the Civil Service and the Bank should be raised by 6% to allow for their non-contributory pension schemes. In the case of the Bank one year's seniority is granted for entrants with G.C.E. 'A' level passes in approved subjects. The Bank scale is the same for men and women to age 23; after that women are paid on the lower scale. The age links in the Local Government scale are notional (i.e. staff may receive accelerated increments).

in 1954, the Treasury representatives said of the Civil Service that it 'must be able to recruit its fair share of the available talent in all classes. From this point of view, the rates currently offered for similar work by outside employers are of paramount importance.'[17] This is equally true for administrators and clerical workers in the hospital service.

Salaries, although of basic importance, are however only one aspect of a recruitment policy. Alongside the inadequacy of the rates of pay in the hospital service there were, in our view, other reasons why hospital authorities failed to attract young men into hospital administration in the period 1945–59, and some of these were not outside their control.

Changed Social Conditions Affecting Recruitment

We attribute the failure mainly to their not being so quick as were many other employers of labour to understand the consequence of the social and economic changes which occurred in our society after 1939. During and after the Second World War there were many more employment opportunities open to young people. As a result of this the hospital service (along with many other public services) lost some of the 'attractiveness' which it formerly had for prospective administrative and clerical workers. A further effect of full employment has been that whereas, before the war, young people might remain at school after taking their School Certificate examinations until a job presented itself, now the output of our schools and universities has already been snapped up by the more percipient employers before the end of the school or university year.

Concurrently with the effects of full employment, the impact of the 1944 Education Act has forced employers generally to change their recruitment plans. As the Act became effective more and more of precisely those boys who before the war were recruited into hospitals from grammar schools remained at school until 18 and then proceeded to the universities. Thus they were no longer available as recruits to hospital administration before they were 21 or (during the period of National Service) 23 and, only then, if hospital authorities were willing to recruit young graduates to their staff.

Another post-war condition affecting the number of young people available for employment in hospital administration is their changed attitude to other forms of occupation. Before the war the social status of a 'white-collared' worker was probably higher than it now is relative to that of the general body of workers. This change in social attitudes has had significant effects and has been commented upon by observers in fields of employment comparable to the hospital service. Typical of these comments is the one made by Political and Economic Planning in 1956: 'Industry's mounting claims on graduate labour have presented other employers, not least the Civil Service . . . with recruitment problems the solution of which is not yet in sight.'[18] Reference may also be made to *The Times* editorial and news item of the 5th October 1956 and some subsequent correspondence. An observation made in 1961 makes a similar admission. It (i.e. the Civil Service) 'has recently had some difficulty in recruiting enough staff of the right quality for almost every one of its classes.'[19]

We have referred to these other factors affecting the availability of young recruits to the hospital service in order to emphasize that salary, though of basic importance, is not the only determinant of the recruiting power of hospital authorities. That this is so has been demonstrated during the post-war years by a number of hospital administrators who, notwithstanding the adverse salary rates, have been able to engage grammar school and university leavers by 'going into the market' at the time these young people were seeking employment, and by informing them of the possibilities of employment in hospital administration and by offering to provide them with some form of training.

In saying that hospital authorities have been slow to recognize the social and economic changes which have taken place since 1939 we are understating our case. The truth is that many hospital authorities are still not alive to the effects these changes have made on their recruitment potential. It is, for instance, only within the last year or two that there is any evidence that hospital authorities, apart from the isolated initiative of a few individuals, have recognized the importance of recruiting towards the end of the school year. This was recognized by the Sheffield Regional Staff Advisory Committee in June 1960[20] and by the North-East Metropolitan Region at about the same time, and in these two regions and others there is now a system of consolidated advertising for junior staff in the spring of each year. The Liverpool Region has a joint recruitment pamphlet.

On the experience of the Sheffield Regional Staff Advisory Committee, Mr. Maurice Naylor, the Deputy Secretary of the Sheffield Regional Hospital Board, observes: 'One of the object lessons in the Sheffield experiment in recruiting school leavers is that a Service which is *obviously* a Service and not a number of individual and small authorities is more attractive and offers better training facilities and better career prospects. Indeed the main achievement of the Sheffield experiment was the grouping of hospitals on a co-operative basis where they delegated their responsibility for making appointments of school leavers to a Committee representative of all the authorities, thus sacrificing some of their autonomy.'[21]

The foregoing strictures about the lack in general of a recruitment policy for young men refer mainly to the failure of the hospital service to attract suitable grammar school leavers. It is a moot point, however, whether under the changed post-war conditions the grammar schools can be the major source of recruitment as they were before 1939.

The failure of hospital authorities themselves to recognize the desirability and necessity to look to other sources such as the universities for potential administrators was corrected in part by the initiative of the Ministry of Health, who in 1956 obtained the National Health Service Administrative and Clerical Staffs Whitley Council's agreement to the intake of sixteen young men or women a year into a 'National Training Scheme' for hospital administrators.[22] Most, though not all, of these were from the universities. This number was increased to twenty-four in 1961 and rose to fifty-five this year (1962) with the advent of the Ministry's sponsored Regional Training Schemes.[23] Both the 'National' and 'Regional' Schemes are open to in-service candidates. In 1962, ten in-service candidates were selected.

Thus it is only now in 1962 that the hospital service is at long last beginning to face the implications of developments which have taken place since 1939.

Effect on Recruitment of Establishment Control

It has been represented to us that hospital authorities' initiative in recruitment was inhibited from 1951 to 1959 by the strict control of establishments during that period. Undoubtedly this made their task difficult, but nevertheless throughout the whole of the years 1948 to 1960 there was, except in 1950 and 1952, an expansion in administrative and clerical staff. For all staff (including typists and machine operators) this amounted in total to a 49% increase over the twelve years. It is true that 29% of the expansion took place in the years 1948–50 and that in all probability a very substantial part of the

49% has been in female typing and clerical staff associated with medical records.[24] Increases have also been necessitated by the need to meet Ministry requirements with respect to finance records, stores and inventory checking and so on. Nevertheless, within the much smaller expansion of administrative and clerical staff (other than for these purposes and in medical records' departments), and the opportunities provided by vacancies occurring as a result of labour turnover, it should have been possible for hospital Boards and Committees to secure a more even distribution of staff over the age structures if they had pursued a recruitment policy having this as one of its objectives.

The fact is that throughout the period 1948–60 the expansion and labour turnover have led—as we have demonstrated—to the admission of a disproportionately large number of staff in their late twenties and early thirties, and it is these who now form a considerably oversized block in the middle portion of the male age structure.

Need for Recruitment Policy

From this past experience, if for no other reason, two objectives seem to be manifestly clear—

(1) That the hospital service should have a recruitment policy for its administrative and clerical staff.

(2) That this policy should take account of the existing age structures and should be designed to preclude a repetition of events like those of the past twenty years.

We devote our next chapter to supplying information and making calculations about the recruitment needs of the Service. Information and calculations of this kind are essential if the objectives we have suggested are to be attained.

Chapter 4   Recruitment Needs

As part of the survey we have attempted to estimate the numbers of administrative and clerical staff which the hospital service needs to recruit in the coming years.

Experience in other branches of the hospital service (notably medical staffing) has shown that such estimating is a somewhat hazardous undertaking and that faulty forecasts lead to trouble both for the Service and the staff affected. Since planning is an important part of administration it would seem especially appropriate that administrators should endeavour to calculate recruitment needs in their own ranks with as much precision as possible.

For this purpose it is not sufficient to rely upon age tables such as those contained in our Appendices 3 and 4. Some hospital administrative and clerical staff (e.g. those whose superannuation rights derive from the pre-appointed day mental health authorities) have the option of retiring at 55, and all staff (either under the NHS Superannuation Scheme or the Federated Superannuation Scheme for Nurses and Hospital Officers) can retire at 60 or remain at work to the age of 65. In view of these possibilities we asked staff to state their 'anticipated year of retirement'. The resultant numbers of anticipated retirements of existing staff for each year to 2009 are given in Appendices 43 (men) and 44 (women).

Based on these returns some estimates can be made of the recruitment that will be necessary to replace retiring staff. Our estimates do not take account of such factors as vacancies created by staff leaving or deaths occurring before the anticipated date of retirement, or any further expansion of the labour force; neither do they allow for the, at present, unpredictable effect of developments envisaged in the Ministry's recently published Hospital Plan for England and Wales.[25]

We have considered trying to calculate the effects of the Hospital Plan. This may (or it may not) result in a reduction of administrative and clerical staff upon the closure of smaller hospitals and the projected amalgamation of some groups. One immediate effect is, in fact, an increase of regional staffs concerned with planning. We have also considered allowing for other special developments in the Service. For example, there may be on the one hand increases in staff concerned with the application of work study, and on the other hand reductions as a result of the introduction of automation in accounting procedures.

Obviously allowances must be made for developments of this kind but we decided to confine ourselves to making estimates related to the situation as it was at the time of our survey. Hospital authorities may wish to adjust our estimates up or down according to their own calculations of the outcome of current or prospective special developments.

The incidence of vacancies created by staff leaving or deaths occurring before the anticipated date of retirement could be calculated if staff records had been kept in the past. In the absence of staff records we have not added to our estimates to cover these contingencies. Life Offices could probably supply information about the incidence of death and disabling illness or accident before age 60 but we have not obtained this. In Appendix 46 we give statistics of staff wastage in the civil service. From these it seems to us that our basic estimates of recruitment needs should be increased by, perhaps, 20% to cover deaths or vacancies before retirement.

We have analysed the numbers contained in Appendices 43 and 44 so as to distinguish the recruitment needs in two main groups of staff:

(1) the General Administrative grade and above;
(2) the male clerical staff.

We have made this broad division because these are the two main groups into which the staff divide from the point of view of careers; it is our opinion that recruitment needs should be considered in the light of this fact. As we show in Chapter 5 the majority of the designated and administrative grades are career staff. Male clerical staff are also career-minded although many of these have limited career ambitions and prospects. It is because of these limitations that we have treated the male clerical staff separately from the more senior grades. A large majority of female staff (see pages 54–55 and 63–64) are apparently not career-minded. For this reason and also because, in our view, the estimates are liable to be falsified by the effects of marriage and motherhood we have made no estimates based on the figures for female staff given in Appendix 44.

Recruitment Needs in the Designated, Senior and General Administrative Grades

In these grades (more so perhaps than in the clerical grades) it does not follow that a man is succeeded in his post by a man, or a woman by a woman. For this reason we amalgamated the numbers of men and women in these grades shown separately in our Appendices (in fact, in a total of 1,016 staff in these grades only 57 are women). We also summarized the anticipated retirals into five-year periods starting in 1961–65 and then calculated the percentage of the totals by grades which would be retiring in each five-year period. The results are given in Table 10.

As it is clearly impossible to forecast them, we do not allow in this Table, and in Tables 11 and 12, for the consequences of promotion from one grade to another; nor do we allow for the changes which will result from the appointment of new staff. Thus the percentages in Table 10 relate to the staff *at present* in the grades shown. We have given the details contained in Table 10 so as to show how we derive the estimates contained in Table 11. The pattern revealed by these estimates will change from year to year as new staff are appointed and as promotion takes place from the lower to the higher grades. For example, if, on the retirement of 214 Designated Officers in the period 1961–65 (Table 11), all those appointed to take their place were from the 273 staff who are at present in the Senior Administrative grade and due to retire in 1976–80, the figures of 446 Designated Officers and 273 Senior Administrative grade in that quinquennium would become 660 and 59 respectively. If the 214 Senior Administrative posts thus vacated were filled by 214 of the 493 General Administrative staff due to retire in 1976–80, the figures in that line would be 660, 273, 179. But the total of 1,212 for 1976–80 would remain the same. If, however, these 214 Senior Administrative posts were filled, say, by General Administrative staff due to retire in 1981–85 the figures on the fourth and fifth lines of the Table would be:

	D	SA	GA	Total
1976–80	660	59	493	1,212
1981–85	190	495	383	1,068

In each case the totals remain the same. The totals are therefore the important figures in Table 11. These totals will be affected by promotion from the clerical grades. Such promotions may be of men or women. If, however, the hospital service continues to promote only a very small percentage of women into the administrative and designated grades nearly all the promotions from the clerical grades will be of men.

For this reason and also because the estimates for men are more dependable than those for women, our calculations in Table 12 are confined to male clerical staff only.

Table 10 *Designated and Administrative Grades*

Percentage of staff in the survey group retiring in each quinquennial period commencing 1961–65.

Period	Grade of staff		
	D	SA	GA
1961–65	11·7	5·5	4·4
1966–70	17·7	8·5	9·2
1971–75	27·3	17·4	14·3
1976–80	24·6	23·8	17·9
1981–85	10·5	24·4	21·7
1986–90	7·2	13·4	17·4
1991–95	0·9	6·0	10·3
1996–00		1·0	4·6
2001–05			0·2

In our four regions taken together the percentage response from staff in the designated and administrative grades was: 60% General Administrative, 67% Senior Administrative and 80% Designated Officers, i.e. from these grades the response was especially good. We have assumed, therefore, that the proportions shown in Table 10 are probably representative for all staff in the designated and administrative grades, and we have applied them to the national totals of men and

Table 11 *Estimated Quinquennial Retirals of Persons in the Designated and Administrative Grades* (England and Wales)

Period	Grade			Total quinquennial retirals	Approximate annual replacement*
	D	SA	GA		
1961–65	214	63	121	398	80
1966–70	321	98	253	672	134
1971–75	495	200	393	1,088	218
1976–80	446	273	493	1,212	242
1981–85	190	281	597	1,068	214
1986–90	131	154	479	764	153
1991–95	16	69	283	368	74
1996–00		11	126	137	27
2001–05			5	5	1
Totals	1,813	1,149	2,750	5,712	

* See comments immediately following Table 13.

women in these grades. This gives us for England and Wales as a whole the estimates of staff retirals in each of the nine quinquennial periods shown in Table 11.

Before we comment on Table 11 we give here our estimates of the recruitment needs for male clerical staff.

Recruitment Needs in the Male Clerical Grades

In calculating the estimates which follow (Table 12) we have had to make an assumption that a clerical post at present held by a man is filled by a man because it is considered that the work involved in it is more appropriate to a man than to a woman. We realize that some posts now held by men will be filled by women when the existing holder retires or leaves, but the converse could also apply; so we have assumed that the present ratio of men to women in the clerical grades (i.e. 5,912 to 13,896) will probably continue for some time to come and we have made our estimates accordingly. In this matter, as in our contemplation of the possible effects of the Hospital Plan, work study and automation (see page 32), we considered making allowance for possible changes in the future but decided to base our calculations on the facts of the present situation, as far as these are known to us.

Table 12 *Higher Clerical and Clerical Grades (Men)*

Percentage of Staff in the Survey Group Retiring in each Quinquennial Period commencing 1961–65, and
Estimated Quinquennial Retirals (England and Wales)

Period	Percentage of retirals (Survey group)	Estimated retirals (England and Wales)	Approximate annual replacement*
1961–65	4·3	254	51
1966–70	5·8	342	68
1971–75	9·3	550	110
1976–80	8·1	478	96
1981–85	13·1	776	155
1986–90	17·2	1,017	203
1991–95	13·0	769	154
1996–00	11·0	650	130
2001–05	10·2	603	121
2006–10	8·0	473	95
Totals		5,912	

* See comments immediately following Table 13.

Total Recruitment Needs

The total recruitment needs of the Service for the designated and administrative grades and for male clerical staff are estimated in Table 13. When considering these estimates the reader is asked again to note the reservations we make on pages 32 and 33.

Table 13 *Totals of Estimated Retirals (Tables 11 and 12 Combined)*

	a	*b*	*c*	*Approximate annual replacements (see comments below)*
Period	*Designated and admin. grades*	*Clerical grades (men)*	*Total of columns (a) and (b)*	
1961–65	398	254	652	130
1966–70	672	342	1,014	205
1971–75	1,088	550	1,638	328
1976–80	1,212	478	1,690	338
1981–85	1,068	776	1,844	367
1986–90	764	1,017	1,781	356
1991–95	368	769	1,137	227
1996–00	137	650	787	157
2001–05	5	603	608	122
2006–10		473	473	95
Totals	5,712	5,912	11,624	

The figures given in the final column above, and also in the final columns of Tables 11 and 12, are estimates of the average number of recruits required yearly in each quinquennial period if hospital authorities do no more and no less in each period than try to replace the staff retiring during that period. This, in our view, would be a mistaken policy because the ultimate effect might be to produce all over again an unbalanced age structure of the kind from which the hospital service is suffering at present. Figure 11 illustrates how this would happen.

Recruitment Policy to Correct the Existing Age Structure

We have already discussed some of the unfortunate effects of an unbalanced age structure. In our opinion recruitment policy in the hospital service should be designed to correct this, if possible, within, say, the next ten years. This cannot be achieved through the unco-ordi-

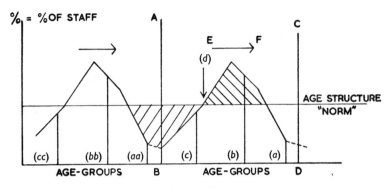

FIGURE 11

The present male age structure is shown to the right of the vertical line AB. It is, of course, a dynamic figure, i.e. it is moving in the direction indicated by the arrow EF past the retiring age at CD. If at each stage as any given age-group retires, e.g. (a) in a few years, (b) in about 1980 and (c) in some forty years from now, the same number of staff, i.e. (aa), (bb), (cc), is recruited at AB (the entry age) then the age structure repeats itself all over again in the process of time.

(d) = upper age-limit of existing 'trough' of male-staff deficiencies. At present this is at about age 31. This is indicated here to illustrate a comment made on page 40.

nated activity of some 429 separate employing authorities.[26] There will have to be some planned policy of recruitment both with respect to the nature and number of the annual intake. It is not at all easy to suggest what this should be.

If the present staff were fairly evenly distributed over the age structure the annual recruitment needs for existing establishments would be approximately 143 for designated and administrative grades and 122 for the male clerical staff. These estimates are based on the existing establishment of 5,712 posts in the designated and administrative grades and 5,912 posts held by male clerical staff. We have assumed a working age-range of 40 years (i.e. 25–64 inclusive) for the former and of 49 years (i.e. 16–64 inclusive) for the latter. The resultant quotients of 143 and 122 correspond closely to the average of the estimated annual replacements shown in Tables 11 and 12.

It will be seen that in making these estimates we are assuming a rather long working age-range, and that allowance should be made for staff retiring before they reach the age of 65 and for the loss to the Service of those who die or leave before retirement. Such allowances should be made (see page 32). The figures referred to here should be regarded as basic minima.

Table 11 shows that the annual replacement needs for the designated and administrative grades will be less than the minimal 143 for the next ten years and more than this for the period 1971–90. Replacement needs for male clerical staff will be less than the minimal 122 a year until 1980 (Table 12) and thereafter more for the following twenty years. The 'peaks' of outgoing staff are in the period 1976–80 for the designated and administrative grades and 1986–90 for the clerical grades.

The only radical way to correct the imbalance of the existing age structure would be to offer early retirement on favourable terms to the 'excess' staff now in the age range of approximately 31–55 (in ten years' time 41–65), and to recruit new entrants in appropriate numbers at each age throughout the age-range, as it now is, of 16–31 or, as it would be in ten years' time, of 26–41. The effect of this would be to replace the cross-hatched upper peak in Figure 11 by recruits appointed to fill the deficiencies represented by the lower cross-hatched trough.

For the moment we are considering methods of correcting the age structure purely from a management point of view. The views of affected staff may be quite different and since these staff are victims of circumstances not of their own making their views must, in our opinion, be fully met.

It would be extraordinarily hard to implement a policy of early retirement but any other single method is also fraught with difficulties.

For example, we estimate that during the current quinquennium (1961–65), taking the designated, administrative and male clerical grades together (Table 13), the Service will be losing some 650 staff on account of retirement. In our view the number which the Service would 'normally' recruit in this period should be no less than 1,290 (i.e. five years at about 258 each year; see page 69). To make possible the recruitment of the difference between this number and the 650 posts falling vacant would necessitate a temporary increase in the establishment of 640 posts. Similar conditions in the period 1966–70 would necessitate a further temporary increase of about 280 posts. These additional 920 posts, created in the ten years 1961–70, would anticipate the position as we think it will be after 1971, from about which date there will be a substantial excess of vacancies over the estimated norm in each five-year period for over twenty years. For example, in the years 1971–1980 some 3,330 posts will be falling vacant against the norm for ten years of 2,580. This excess demand of 750 could in theory be met from the 920 additional staff recruited in the previous decade. In practice, however, the 'additional posts' would in all probability have come to be regarded as normal establishment, and there would be a demand above these for the filling of all the posts currently becoming vacant during 1971–80. One method by which this difficulty could be met without making a temporary increase of 920 posts in the period 1961–70 would be, throughout these years, to appoint junior career staff to posts hitherto held by short-stay staff. A weakness in this suggestion is, of course, that such posts are usually of a 'non-career' type and not suitable for junior trainees and there would be little likelihood of attracting the right kind of recruits to them.

Yet another difficulty is presented by the trough in the age structure under age 31. To fill this would entail recruiting staff in appropriate numbers over the whole age-range of 16 to 31, or possibly with passing years over an even greater age-range, i.e. as the point at (d) on Figure 11 moves in the direction EF. This need to recruit staff over an age-range of up to 31 or more is not entirely consistent with a policy of taking school leavers at 16 and 18 and University leavers at, say, 21 or 22. There may, however, be a case for taking some entrants in their late twenties or even (later on) in their early thirties. This, we believe, might be particularly applicable in finance administration for which, as we shall see later (page 60), there may be special staffing problems. But there will nevertheless be a difficulty in regulating the intake at the various age-levels involved. This difficulty would be lessened if staffing records were maintained which indicated the numbers required in different age-groups and if, in default of a central or regional recruiting agency, hospital authorities could be advised from time to time of the Service's requirements.

Despite the difficulties we have referred to, the hospital service could bring its age structure into a less irregular condition if it adopted a combination of remedies. Some method of favourable early retirement might be introduced for any staff who wished to accept it; any further expansion of the labour force[27] would go part of the way to meeting the need for 'additional posts' in the next ten-year period; advantage could also be taken of staff wastage prior to retirement to correct the age structure, provided this and any future expansion of the labour force were used to recruit staff at those points in the age-range where there are deficiencies, and to avoid any additions where there are excesses.

40

A combination of these methods as part of a carefully considered policy of staff recruitment and retirement could secure a less irregular age structure within a period of ten years, and this could be maintained if annual recruitment followed the principles which we have suggested.

We said earlier that we were considering the correction of the age structure from a management point of view. In the long run it is equally important to the staff that the imbalance should be corrected. On pages 17 and 18 we reviewed some of the undesirable effects of the present conditions. These cannot be corrected without affecting the position of some sections of staff, but the livelihood and the status and income of individual members must be adequately protected if changes are to secure the agreement of the staff associations.

Reform of the Present Staffing Structure

In this chapter we have been considering the hospital service's recruitment needs in terms of the existing staff structure. There have been some amendments to this from time to time since 1948[28] but fundamentally the structure is still based on concepts contained in original memoranda issued by the Ministry of Health in 1947 and 1948.[29] These memoranda made no clear distinction between administrative and clerical work and hitherto there has been an underlying assumption that, generally speaking, administrators were to be recruited through the clerical grades.[30] The prospect of advancement to administrative work from the clerical grades should be retained for young clerical staff who show special aptitudes and ability. The retention of this possibility is not, however, inconsistent with a major reform of the present structure. In our view the time has come when such a reform should be made. In an Epilogue to this report we offer our suggestions on what should be done and the effects that the reform would have upon recruitment policy.

Chapter 5 Mobility

The hospital service in England and Wales is made up of 429 comparatively small independent employing authorities.[31] In consequence administrative and clerical staff who desire promotion usually have to be prepared to move from one authority to another to secure it, and also to gain the kind of experience which will make them eligible for promotion. The questionnaire contained a number of questions designed to discover something about mobility, e.g. the proportion of people who had attempted to move, how many had succeeded and whether there were any geographic limitations to staff movement. We also wanted to find out which of the many factors that affect mobility were those that most frequently prompted or prevented the movement of hospital administrators.

In considering this chapter some allowance should be made for the possibility that in our sample (compared with those who are not included) there may be higher proportions of staff who are mobile or potentially mobile. If this is so, our findings will suggest a greater degree of mobility than is to be found among staff as a whole. The effect of this possible bias will not, we think, be great in the designated and administrative grades because of the substantial response we received from them but should be borne in mind in relation to the figures for clerical staff.

Table 14 *Percentage of Male (Administrative and Clerical) Staff Making Applications for Employment with Other Hospital Authorities* (1948 *to* 1960)

Number of applications submitted to other authorities	Year recruited			Overall 1948–60
	Pre-1952	1952–55	1956–60	
	%	%	%	%
Nil	30	33	66	38
1–5	37	48	30	37 ⎤
6–10	16	11	3	12 ⎬ 62
11 +	17	8	1	13 ⎦
Total (= 100%)	1,202	157	356	1,715
	Year of recruitment not known			11
				1,726

42

Male Staff

Applications Submitted

Appendix 15 shows (by grades) how many applications male staff have submitted since 1948 for jobs in hospital authorities other than their own. For the sake of precision we divided staff into three groups —those recruited before 1952; those recruited during the period 1952–1955; those who entered the service after 1955. The details given in Appendix 15 under these three headings are summarized for all staff taken together in Table 14.

Of the staff recruited before 1952 and those recruited in 1952–1955, Table 15 shows the percentages by grades of those who have made no applications, one application, and two or more.

Table 15 *Percentage of Male (Administrative and Clerical) Staff, by Grades, Applying for Other Posts*

(The term 'other posts' here, and in Tables 16 and 25, means posts other than with an employee's own Board or Hospital Management Committee.)

Period of recruitment	Grade	No. of staff (=100%)	No applications	One application	Two applications or more
			%	%	%
Staff recruited before 1952	Designated	317	26	10	64
	Senior Administrative	184	26	8	66
	General Administrative	362	26	10	65
	Higher Clerical	266	34	9	57
	Clerical	73	62	8	30
	All staff taken together	1,202	30	9	61
Staff recruited 1952–55	Designated	6	33	17	50
	Senior Administrative	8	38		62
	General Administrative	31	10	13	77
	Higher Clerical	69	30	10	60
	Clerical	43	54	16	30
	All staff taken together	157	33	12	55

Having in this way obtained some indication of the proportions of staff who had attempted to move, we then considered the amount of movement which has actually taken place since 1948.

Movement Since 1948

From Appendix 19 we calculate in Table 16 the proportions of staff in each grade who, since 1948 (or from the date on which they entered the Service, whichever is the more recent) have made no move, one move, and two moves or more.

Table 16 *Percentage of Male (Administrative and Clerical) Staff, by Grades, Who Have Moved to Other Posts*

Grade	No. of staff (= 100%)	No move	One move	Two moves or more
		%	%	%
Designated . . .	330	58	18	24
Senior Administrative .	196	58	18	24
General Administrative .	433	64	19	17
Higher Clerical . .	444	74	17	9
Clerical . . .	323	92	5	3
All staff taken together .	1,726	70	16	14

Since movement is normally associated with promotion the high percentage of non-movers in the clerical grade is self-explanatory. What little movement there has been in this grade is due either to promotion before July 1958, when the lettered grades were replaced by the new grading structure, or to promotion from an ancillary staff grade.

The picture presented by Table 16 is not altogether satisfactory for a Service in which administrative staff usually have to make a number of moves to gain promotion, and in view of the diversity of experience demanded by the many comparatively small employing authorities. This is particularly true of the figures revealed for the Higher Clerical and General Administrative grades which, before the recent introduction of the Junior Administrative grade, were the nearest approach the hospital service had to training grades.

We cannot, unfortunately, give the proportions of staff making applications to move at various times, nor have we assessed the proportions of people who have moved at different times.

From a consideration of the number of applications submitted (Tables 14 and 15) it seems that the comparative lack of mobility is by no means entirely or even mainly due to the failure of staff to attempt to move. If we assume that the submission of one application signifies a readiness to move (this is, perhaps, a generous assumption and some allowance should be made accordingly) then no less than 62% of all staff (the percentages are higher for the designated and administrative grades) have at some time or other been willing to move, but only 30% have been able to do so in the whole of the period 1948–60. Thus, in broad terms, we can say for the male staff as a whole:

30% wanted to move at some time or other and have moved;
32% wanted to move at some time or other but haven't been able to;
38% have not tried to move.

Movement Affected by Age and Marital Status

We believe that the most important factor affecting mobility is age. We have already discussed at some length the peculiarities of the existing male age structure. The relatively high age level of staff, including those in the 'junior' grades where movement would normally be the greatest, means that a large number of staff have domestic responsibilities and ties which would not ordinarily be found among staff in these grades. For instance, the median of the ages of men in the General Administrative grade is 40 and in consequence (see Table 17) nearly all of these are married and have children (74% of them of school age). In these circumstances it is perhaps surprising that such a high proportion of the men in this grade (75% to 90%: see Table 15) are potentially mobile.

Table 17 summarizes details of the marital status of males given in Appendix 21.

Table 17 *Summary of Marital Status of Male Staff in the Survey Group*

State	Grade					Total
	DO	SA	GA	HC	C	
Married ⎫ Widowed ⎬ . Divorced ⎭	319	185	393	361	170	1,428
Single .	11	11	40	83	153	298
	330	196	433	444	323	1,726

These figures plainly illustrate the point we have just made. In the General Administrative and Higher Clerical grades, in which there would normally be a high degree of mobility, approximately 91% and 81% of the staff are married. If we accept the limitations of the median as a satisfactory measure of location where the range of ages is so great, then the average marrying age of staff in the General Administrative and Higher Clerical grades is 25 (Appendix 21(b)). Only 12 General Administrative staff (i.e. 4%) in a known total of 332, and 77 Higher Clerical staff (i.e. 23%) in a known total of 328, were unmarried at the time of their promotion to these grades (Appendix 8). In other words it is quite usual for a man to be married before he even secures promotion to the Higher Clerical grade.

Marriage normally brings with it responsibilities for housing and children. It was upon these two responsibilities that we concentrated in our questionnaire.

Housing and Children

It will be seen that question 12 of our questionnaire was, in effect, an attitude survey and the results of this are given in Appendix 22. Taken together, 602 married men in the General Administrative and Higher Clerical grades replied to this question and 425 (i.e. 71%) gave 'Housing' as a factor that had affected their decisions in contemplating movement. Of all the married men in these two grades— 62% are buying or have bought a house or flat; 15% are renting a council house or flat; another 15% are renting a private house or flat; 6% live in 'other' types of housing (including hospital accommodation) and 2% said they were living with parents or relatives (Appendix 25). In these days of continued difficulty in obtaining housing accommodation and of the relatively high costs of house purchase and of associated fees and charges, it is not surprising that housing should rank highest among the factors which affect a married man's decision whether or not to move.

Appendix 26 shows the number of children in relation to the number of married males. 87% of Designated Officers, 82% of Senior and General Administrative Officers and 62% of Higher Clerical and Clerical staff, who are married, have children. 78% of the children of these staff are of school age or above. 'Children's schooling' came third after 'Housing' and 'Lack of Financial Incentive' in the answers from the married males to our question on factors affecting mobility (Appendix 22).

Table 18 summarizes the response to that question, showing as percentages of the total answers received, the relative weight attached to the various factors which we listed in the questionnaire.

Table 18 *Factors Affecting Mobility Among Married Male (Administrative and Clerical) Staff*

Factors	No. of times mentioned as a % of total answers received	
	Married	*Single*
	%	%
Housing	29	8
Children's Schooling . .	16	
Dependent Relatives . .	8	27
Lack of Financial Incentive .	25	39
Lack of Removal Allowance .	14	7
Other Reasons . . .	8	18

We have so far concerned ourselves with the effect on mobility of age, marital state, housing and children, and in Table 18 we have indicated some other factors which also have a bearing on a man's willingness to move.

Ambition

Whether or not a man is prepared to surmount or ignore handicaps to movement will very much depend upon the extent of his ambition. It is, of course, very difficult to assess this through the medium of a questionnaire.   After experimenting with draft questionnaires on several groups of hospital administrators who were known to us, we decided that some idea could be obtained by asking the two following questions:

What grade do you expect to reach before retirement?

Would you be prepared to move to ANY part of the country to further your career?

The answers to the first question are given in Appendix 28. It is clear that nothing needs to be said about the answers given by Designated Officers. In the replies from the other grades we decided to try to distinguish three groups—those who are 'ambitious' in the sense

47

described in the next paragraph, those with 'limited ambition' and those with (seemingly) 'no ambition'. We realize that the attempt to measure degrees of ambition on the basis of comparatively little information may be liable to more than a small margin of error. We were satisfied, however, from the trials we made with our draft questionnaires that a broad guide to staffs' ambitions could be gained if we adopted the following definitions:

For our purposes, staff are said to be 'ambitious' if they are in the Senior Administrative grade and expect to reach a senior designated post, or if they are in the General Administrative grade and expect to reach a designated post (senior or junior), or if they are in one of the clerical posts and expect to reach the Senior Administrative grade or above; those with 'limited ambition' in our definition are staff in the Senior Administrative grade who expect to reach a junior designated post; those in the General Administrative grade who expect to reach the Senior Administrative grade, and those in the clerical grades who expect to reach the General Administrative grade. 'No ambition' we have ascribed to those who expect to go no further than their present grade or no further than Higher Clerical if they are in the Clerical grade at present. Ambitions are not in all cases identical with expectations, but we found that the latter gave us a fairly reliable guide to the former.[32]

By applying our definitions to the data contained in Appendix 28

Table 19 *Ambitions of Male (Administrative and Clerical) Staff in the Survey Group by Grades*

Possession of:	SA	GA	HC	C(a)
	%	%	%	%
'Ambitious' (d) .	45	48	49	45
Limited ambition	41	38	36	22 (b)
No ambition .	14	14	15	33 (c)

(a) A comparison of this column with that for the South Western region alone (i.e. the region in which there was the highest response from clerical staff) indicates that had there been a higher response from the clerical staff in the other three regions the proportion at (b) would be considerably more than 22% and at (c) correspondingly less than 33%.

(d) See definition above.

(excluding the 'not stated') we obtain the picture presented by Table 19.

This analysis in Table 19 suggests that whilst there is no serious lack of ambition in administrative and clerical staff in the hospital service, more than 50% of them have at most only a limited amount of ambition. This is, of course, not necessarily a bad thing. If a very high proportion of staff in these grades expected to obtain senior posts before their retirement, morale in the Service might suffer because of the disillusionment of those who failed to achieve the positions which they expected to reach. Indeed, it would be unwise for hospital authorities to attempt to fill their ranks entirely or even largely with men who aspired to designated posts.

The facts illustrated in Table 19 undoubtedly have a bearing on mobility for it seems reasonable to assume that staff who have no ambition are unlikely to attempt to move unless they desire a change of environment for other reasons. And similarly those with only limited ambition are likely to make only limited attempts to move. A comparison of Table 19 with the first part of Table 15 suggests that less than one-third of the Senior Administrative staff, about one-third of the General Administrative staff and one-half of the Higher Clerical staff, with limited ambition, expect this ambition to be realized as a result of promotion within the employment of their own hospital authority without the necessity of movement.

Geographic Bars to Mobility

The answers to our question 'Would you be prepared to move to ANY part of the country to further your career?' are given in Appendix 29. A comparison of the figures for married men with those for single men supports our views about the effect on mobility of marriage. Whereas 55% of the single men in the survey group are willing to move to any part of the country, only 35% of married men are prepared to do so.

In the second part of the question about preparedness to move we asked staff, other than those who said they were prepared to move anywhere, to specify the areas which held no attraction for them. In response to this we had the following number of answers. This analysis was made manually and we could not readily differentiate men from women. In this instance, therefore, our numbers relate to both male and female staff:

Answers	Region
255	Liverpool
530	North-East Metropolitan
420	Sheffield
1,102	South Western
2,307	

The numbers of times particular areas were mentioned expressed as percentages of the total answers received by regions are listed in Table 20. The first entry, 'no move, etc.', includes people who were not prepared to move at all (reason not stated), those who were not prepared to move because of age, and those who were prepared to move but only within the area of their own region. In the case of the North-East Metropolitan staff the last category was taken to include London

Table 20 *Geographic Bars to Mobility*
Number of references to particular areas expressed as percentages
of total answers received (Men and Women)

Area	Region				Total
	Liverpool	*North-East Metropoli- tan*	*Sheffield*	*South Western*	
	%	%	%	%	%
No move or move only in area of the region . .	34	23	20	17	21
North . .	12	31	26	28	26
Midlands . .	11	21	7	18	16
London . .	13	2	12	11	9
Wales . .	4	5	7	5	5
Scotland . .	7	2	7	4	5
'Industrial areas' (area unspecified)	6	7	9	10	9
'Large Towns' (area unspecified)	4	2	3	3	3
Other places .	9	7	9	4	6
	100	100	100	100	100
Totals of answers received . .	255	530	420	1,102	2,307

as a whole. The 2% in this region not prepared to move to London is of staff in the non-metropolitan part of the region.

To us the surprising results in Table 20 were the percentages against the first entry ('no moves, etc.') for the Liverpool and South Western Regions. This high percentage in Liverpool may be attributable to the fact that this is the 'most concentrated' of the regions and in consequence it is possible for staff to gain additional experience or promotion by movement to other hospital authorities without changing their residence. We are at a loss to account for the small percentage under this heading in the South Western Region unless it is that this is a region with a large number of small hospitals and a relatively high proportion of small authorities. Staff may feel that they need to move out of the region to get promotion.

In Table 21 we have analysed the proportions of the Senior and General Administrative staff and the male clerical grades (both married and single taken together) according to their preparedness to move anywhere.

Table 21 *Preparedness to Move (I)*

Preparedness to move anywhere	Grade				Four grades combined	Total staff (=100%)
	SA	GA	HC	C		
Prepared . .	% 37	% 34	% 41	% 53	% 41	558
Not prepared .	63	66	59	47	59	805

In the category of 'ambitious' as defined on page 48 there are higher proportions stating their preparedness to move anywhere than the percentages for all staff shown in Table 21. The comparative figures are:

Table 22 *Preparedness to Move (II)*

Prepared to move anywhere	Grade				Four grades combined
	SA	GA	HC	C	
Of all staff (as in Table 21)	% 37	% 34	% 41	% 53	% 41
Of 'ambitious' staff .	42	41	50	62	48

To sum up this discussion of the geographic bars to movement—it seems that of all male staff, including senior designated officers (to many of whom movement is a thing of the past), approximately 40% are prepared to move anywhere and that a further 40% are prepared to move but not without regard to the area in which a vacancy occurs. Apparently no more than about 20% are unwilling to move.

If this is so, there can be no suggestion that administrative and clerical staff are to any great extent immobile from choice. Some allowance should be made, however, for the subjective nature of our question on preparedness to move. There may well have been a tendency for some people to give an affirmative answer in the belief that this was expected of them. This is always a possibility with a subjective question and is a bias which cannot be discounted entirely.

If we now relate our findings on the geographic bars to movement to our earlier observations on the number of staff who have attempted to move, and the number who succeeded, we obtain the following picture:

20% of male staff are not willing to move
80% are prepared to move
       half of these are willing to go anywhere
       half put geographic limitations on their willingness to move
62% have attempted to move
30% have succeeded in moving

Wives in Paid Employment

Finally, there is another factor which affects the mobility of married male staff which we tried to assess by asking 'Is your wife engaged in

Table 23 *Proportions of Married Male Staff with Wives in Paid Employment*

	Grade					All staff
	DO	SA	GA	HC	C	
	%	%	%	%	%	%
Wives employed:						
Full-time.	4	15	16	24	30	17
Part-time	11	16	17	20	15	16
Full and Part-time	15	31	33	44	45	33

paid employment?' An analysis of the replies appears in Appendix 30. From this we calculate that the proportions of staff by grades whose wives are working in either full or part-time paid employment are as set out in Table 23.

It is not easy to assess the exact effect which these conditions will have on staff mobility. The amount and nature of the wife's employment will determine the extent to which it may deter or facilitate the husband's mobility. The man whose wife is engaged only part-time in work of a kind which she will almost certainly be able to take up again in another part of the country (e.g. teaching or nursing) might be more ready to move than one whose wife is in full-time employment of a kind in which it would be difficult to secure similar work elsewhere.

On the other hand a married couple with a joint income might be better able to face the costs of a move. A simple correlation of this question on wives' paid employment, with question 13 on preparedness to move to any part of the country, suggests a greater willingness to move among men whose wives are working than among those whose wives are not working. To be meaningful this analysis would have to be taken further to distinguish the men according to age, grade, number and age of children and so on. This is something we have not done.

Another aspect of this problem is that of the member of staff who is himself engaged in some form of remunerative activity outside the hospital service. We have encountered several examples of this especially among the lower-paid grades where a man claims that he is unable to get the standard of living he wants for his family or himself on the income he receives as a hospital officer. In one exceptional instance a higher clerical officer informed us that he was earning more as a part-time instrumentalist in a dance band than he was from his full-time job.

There are also the cases in which both husband and wife are engaged in a joint enterprise. In one such case a hospital secretary owned a small sweet and tobacconist shop, in which his wife served and from which they supplemented his income by an amount greater than the immediate increase he was likely to get upon moving to another hospital authority.

We cannot measure the effects on mobility of wives working in paid employment or of staff themselves having other part-time employment, but it seems likely that for many staff these do have a bearing one way or the other on their preparedness to move.

Applications Submitted

In discussing the mobility of women in administrative and clerical posts we are again in the difficulty we had in considering their recruitment. Such a large percentage (98·3) are clerical staff and so many of these are 'local labour' and short-stay staff that our calculations are not particularly meaningful.

Although of limited value we do show in Table 24 (cf. Table 14 for men) the numbers of applications submitted since 1948 for jobs in other hospital authorities (see Appendix 16).

Table 24 *Percentage of Female (Administrative and Clerical) Staff Making Applications for Employment with Other Hospital Authorities (1948 to 1960)*

Number of applications submitted	Year recruited			Overall 1948–60
	Pre-1952	1952–55	1956–60	
	%	%	%	%
Nil . . .	70	77	88	79
1–5 . . .	26	22	11	19
6 + . . .	4	1	1	2
Total (= 100%) .	503	256	572	1,331
	Year of recruitment not known			25
				1,356

And for comparison with Table 15 (for men), we also give in Table 25 percentages, by grades, of those who have made no applications, one application and two or more.

The numbers in the case of Designated and Senior Administrative Staff in the top half of this Table and of General Administrative staff in the second part are so small as to make the percentages in these cases of no great significance. For the rest it will be seen that compared with male staff of the same grades there has been little attempted movement except by some of the General Administrative staff recruited before 1952.

This lack of movement is confirmed by the data contained in Appendix 20 (Appointments obtained). 1,166 of female staff in a

Table 25 *Percentage of Female (Administrative and Clerical) Staff, by Grades, Applying for Other Posts*

Period of recruitment	Grade	No. of staff ($=100\%$)	No applications	One application	Two applications or more
			%	%	%
	Designated . .	4	50		50
Staff recruited before 1952	Senior Administrative	6	83		17
	General Administrative	40	53	15	32
	Higher Clerical .	201	67	12	21
	Clerical . .	252	76	11	13
	All staff taken together	503	70	12	18
Staff recruited 1952–55	Designated Senior Administrative General Administrative	5	60		40
	Higher Clerical .	62	66	18	16
	Clerical . . .	189	82	13	5
	All staff taken together	256	77	14	9

total of 1,356 (i.e. 86%) have not moved to another authority since they entered hospital employment, or since 1948 if they were in the Service on that date. The majority of women in clerical posts are, as we said earlier, 'local labour'. By this we mean that they are attached to the place in which they are recruited and they wish to remain there. This can be said also of some men but there is apparently a much higher proportion of such staff among women.

Chapter 6 Education and Training

A great deal has been written recently about the training of hospital administrators, for example, articles in *The Hospital* in February, March and September, 1961,[33] and the Study Group Statement of the senior officers attending a course at the University of Leeds in 1960.[34] It is not our intention to add to this discussion here. Instead we hope to give some indications of the educational standards of staff, the number with professional or advanced educational qualifications, and how many have already received some form of training. In brief we shall try to provide information upon which hospital authorities themselves can consider the educational and training needs of the Service.

In this chapter (as in Chapter 4) some allowance should be made for a possible bias in our findings relating to clerical staff (see page 42).

Male Staff

Schooling and Further Education

Appendix 31 deals with the level of general education reached by staff. Table 26, based on the figures given in that Appendix, gives in percentage terms the levels reached by male staff in the survey group on completion of their full-time education.

Table 26 *General Educational Levels (Men)*

Educational level	% of sample
University	3
Grammar or Public School . .	60
Technical or Commercial School .	9
Secondary Modern School	
(or equivalent) . . .	10
Elementary School . . .	15
Other types of education . .	3
Total staff (= 100%) . .	1,726

Question 16 in the questionnaire asked for details of education undertaken after staff had commenced their working careers. Appendix 33 sets out the figures produced by the response to that question. Calculations based on these figures are given in Table 27.

Table 27 *Education Undertaken Since Commencement of Working Career (Men)*

Type	% of sample
University	7
Technical or Commercial College Courses .	54
Correspondence Courses	55
Other	8
Total staff (= 100%)	1,726

These percentages are inclusive: persons who had, for instance, taken a technical college course and also a correspondence course are counted twice.

297 respondents had undertaken no form of further education whatsover. This figure represents 17% of the total sample.

Educational Attainments

It is a convention of the present day to judge a person's education not by his general performance whilst at school, college or university, but rather by his examination performance. This may well mean that employers, and even society as a whole, are rejecting the services of many people of good calibre because of their lack of formal qualifications. Possibly they accept less worthy people because they hold acceptable qualifications. However, in a survey of this nature, where the personal data make it extremely difficult to assess an individual's potential, inevitably we have had to turn to the examination records of the sample.

The figures given in Table 28 are taken from Appendix 35 and show the percentage of male staff, by grades, who have reached certain levels of attainment in school (or equivalent) examinations.

It is not easy to come to any conclusions about the figures in Table 28, especially since the age structure of the individual grades is different from what it would normally be (see Chapter 2). Nevertheless it is probably true to say that the general educational standard of many post-war recruits is lower than that of their predecessors. We have referred to the present tendency to attach increasing importance to the possession of educational qualifications. It is possible that some of the teenagers in the clerical grade (but in the male staff these are relatively

57

Table 28 *Basic Educational Attainment (Men) by Examinations*

Grade	Total staff (= 100%)	GCE 'A' level (+ equivalent)	GCE 'O' level (5 or more subjects) (+ equivalent)	GCE 'O' level (less than 5 subjects)	Exams. of 'similar' standard	No exams. passed
		%	%	%	%	%
Designated Officers	330	6	62	2	7	23
Senior and General Administrative	629	7	48	4	10	31
Higher Clerical and Clerical	767	5	28	17	6	44
All grades	1,726	6	42	9	7	36

few) are still studying for GCE subjects. It should also be remembered, however, that some of the recently recruited younger members of the Service have benefited from the greater opportunities afforded under the Education Act of 1944. The above figures do not present an encouraging picture.

It would appear from Table 28, for instance, that about a third of all Higher Clerical and Clerical grade male staff possess the minimal educational standard of five subjects at GCE 'O' level recommended in the Institute of Hospital Administrators' pamphlet 'Recruitment and Qualification'.[35] Indeed the proportion who possess this minimal standard might be less than it appears from the above Table, because we have been unable to differentiate between those holding passes at 'O' level in English Language and either Mathematics or a Science, and those who have not obtained passes in these subjects. The Institute's pamphlet recommended that English Language and either Mathematics or a Science should be two of the five subjects passed at 'O' level.

University and Professional Qualifications

Appendix 37 gives details of the number and grades of staff who have either obtained University or professional qualifications or who are studying for them. Table 29 summarizes this information to distinguish in percentage terms those staff who have undertaken or successfully completed a course of studies from those who, for whatever reason, have made no attempt.

Table 29 *University and Professional Qualifications (Men)*

Grade	Qualified or studying	Others	Total staff (= 100%)
	%	%	
Designated Officers . . .	89	11	330
Senior and General Administrative	58	42	629
Higher Clerical and Clerical . .	22	78	767
			1,726

In the administrative grades, the 42% of men who are neither qualified nor attempting to qualify may be thought to be a disturbingly high proportion. But in these grades (see Epilogue) there are posts which are not 'administrative' and in which the holders are not expected to have qualifications by examination. In the designated grades the situation appears at first sight to be very different but it should be noted that the term 'qualified' in this particular context may also include some staff whose qualifications have been obtained not by examination. Thus with respect to qualifications by examination the picture for designated officers is probably not quite so good as it would appear to be. Although the questionnaire (question 19) made it clear that we wished to know only about qualifications obtained or obtainable by examinations some staff listed their Fellowship of the Institute of Hospital Administrators. Among these there are, we believe, a number to whom the Fellowship was awarded by virtue of their office and not through the medium of the examinations leading first to the Associateship. This is the reason we think that the 89% shown in Table 29 may overstate the proportion of Designated Officers qualified by examination.

A comparison of the data on professional qualifications with those relating to general educational qualifications will show why at least 60% of all staff below designated officer status are neither qualified nor studying for a qualification. Well over half of the people in these grades (57%) do not possess the minimal qualifications necessary to apply for student membership of many of the professional associations which conduct examinations.

A more detailed study of Appendix 37 shows that there are 163 non-designated male staff in the survey who have passed the final examination of the Institute of Hospital Administrators and 124 who are studying for the Institute's examinations. But only 27 people in the non-designated grades have obtained a recognized accountancy qualification, and only 31 are studying for one. This ratio must be viewed in the light of the fact that 35% of the male administrative and clerical staff are employed in finance administration and 534 (i.e. 29%) of the 1,813 designated officers are Chief Financial Officers or Deputies. If the hospital service continues to expect that its treasurers, finance officers and deputies should 'normally possess professional qualifications'[36] action should be taken to remedy the present shortage of students and qualified staff in the non-designated grades, or hospital authorities will have to look outside the Service when appointing senior finance staff in the future.

We originally intended to devote more attention in this report to analysing and commenting on our information relating to finance staff. We heard, however, from Mr. Roy Sidebotham of Manchester University (now Professor of Accountancy in the Victoria University of Wellington, N.Z.) that he was making a survey of Hospital Service Finance Staffs at the request of the Association of Chief Financial Officers. Readers who have a special interest in this division of hospital administration should refer to their recently (1962) published report.[37]

We have suggested earlier that the lack of professionally qualified men is associated with a shortage of men with general educational qualifications. The two are in fact inter-related. Perhaps one of the causes of this state of affairs is the Second World War, although undoubtedly many of the older men had already 'missed the boat' before 1939. In an attempt, however, to get some idea of how many staff claimed to have been handicapped by war conditions we asked (question 18): 'Was your education or professional training adversely affected by the War?' Rather more than 50% of male staff in the survey said that the war had adversely affected their education or professional training (see Appendix 39). Several of those who said 'No' added a note stating that the war had given them opportunities for study and experience which they might not have had otherwise. Question 18 is another example of the subjective type of question and, because of this, we do not attach as much weight to these replies as to the answers given to a factual type of question. Nevertheless, the nature of the age structure suggests that the careers of men in the survey may have been affected by the war. This factor, we feel, should be borne in mind when the subject of qualifications is being discussed. Many of those whose studies were affected by the war have since become qualified but many have not. We feel that judgment should not be too harsh on the latter. This forbearance should not, however, be allowed to develop into an attitude of mind extending to the younger staff in the Service, whose careers were not affected by World War II.

Residential Courses and Training Schemes

The figures given in Appendix 41 show the numbers of staff who have participated in residential courses and training schemes. Calculations based on these figures show that about 7% of all male staff in the sample have participated in a 'formal training scheme' as opposed to what could be termed appreciation courses. The term 'formal training scheme' is taken to include the post-war King's Fund Bursary scheme and the Hospital Administrative Staff College two-year course, the National Training Scheme and various regional and group schemes. More than 70% of the sample have apparently attended no courses or been involved in any training scheme.

Female Staff

Schooling

The levels of general education reached by the women (Appendix 32) do not vary very much from those of the male staff. Table 30 gives in percentage terms the levels reached by female staff in the survey group on completion of their full-time education.

Table 30 *General Educational Levels* (*Women*)

Educational level	*% of sample*	*% of male sample* (*Table* 26)
University	1	3
Grammar or Public School . .	50 ⎫ 60	60 ⎫ 63
Private (and other) . . .	10 ⎭	3 ⎭
Technical or Commercial School .	17 ⎫	9 ⎫
Secondary Modern School		
(or equivalent) . . .	13 ⎬ 39	10 ⎬ 34
Elementary School . . .	9 ⎭	15 ⎭
Total staff (= 100%) . . .	1,356	1,726

Although only 50% received a grammar or public school education, as opposed to 60% of the men, 10% received private education compared with 3% of the men. It is probably more realistic for our present purposes to take the percentages for both types of education together to obtain a fair comparison. This collation brings the female figure to just below that for the male staff. On the other hand a higher percentage of women received their education at technical, secondary modern or elementary schools. In short the general educational background of female staff is not quite so advanced as that of male staff but the difference is not significantly great.

Educational Attainments

When, however, the basic educational attainment standards are examined (Appendix 36), a somewhat unfavourable picture is observed (see Table 31).

Table 31 *Basic Educational Attainments (Women) by Examination*

Grade	Total staff (= 100%)	GCE 'A' level	GCE 'O' Level (5 or more subjects) (+ equivalent)	GCE 'O' Level less than 5 subjects	Exams. equivalent standard	No. exams. passed
Designated and Administrative	57	% 10	% 43	%	% 11	% 36
Higher Clerical and Clerical	1,299	2	28	12	6	52
All grades . .	1,356	3	29	11	6	51

If the above is compared with Table 28 (males) it will be seen that the standard of achievement of the female staff is lower at almost every point. The proportion who have passed no examinations at all is 51% compared with 36% for men. Or to take another comparison: if the symbol of a satisfactory grammar school achievement is taken to be five 'O' level passes or more, the female staff record 29% against the male 42%. If 'A' level passes are added the gap widens, i.e. 32% against 48%. In fact the evidence suggests that the educational quality of the female staff in the survey group is less than that of the males.

Further Education

Similar differences between the attainments of male and female staff emerge when a comparison is made of the education undertaken after commencement of working career. These differences are seen in the percentages given in Table 32 which are the proportions of the total sample who have undertaken various types of further education since commencing work. These percentages are based on the figures contained in Appendix 34.

Table 32 *Education Undertaken Since Commencement of Working Career (Women)*

Type	% of sample	% of male sample (Table 27)
University (full and part-time) .	2	7
Technical/Commercial College Courses (full and part-time)	53	54
Correspondence Courses . .	7	55
Other types of Course . .	8	8
Total staff (= 100%) . .	1,356	1,726

As in the table for male staff the percentages in Table 32 include double counting and are therefore not mutually exclusive.

Only in the case of technical or commercial college courses do women appear to show equal willingness to take up further studies. This is characteristic of both female Clerical and Higher Clerical staff. It is probable that the courses undertaken were of the 'Secretarial' type provided by education authorities for shorthand and copy typists.

In the other forms of further education the proportion is, in general, noticeably less for women. In the case of correspondence courses (the usual mode of tuition for professional qualifications) it is much lower: 7% compared with 55%. The number of female staff who have done nothing to further their education was 532, i.e. 39% of the total sample. This is markedly higher than the 17% recorded for male staff and offers some indication that a much smaller proportion of women have anything approaching a career interest in the hospital service.

University and Professional Qualifications

The impression that only a small number of the female staff are 'career minded' is confirmed when consideration is given to the numbers of female staff who have or are studying for a university or professional qualification. Appendix 38 shows that there are only 70 (5%) staff in a total of 1,356 who are either qualified or studying for a qualification. The reason for this cannot to any great extent be due to the war. Less than 14% say that the war adversely affected their education or professional training (see Appendix 40). It seems reasonable to assume that the number of women in the sample who are career minded must be very small. The assumption seems to be borne out by the data given on participation in vocational courses and training schemes (Appendix 42). These data indicate that less than 6% of all female staff have attended any residential courses or been associated with any training schemes.

Chapter 7 Career Prospects

The appointment or promotion prospects (the career prospects) for any individual applicant for a post clearly depend on many factors. The deciding determinant, in our view, should be his (or her) ability to do the job for which he is a candidate. This will depend in part on factors which, to some extent, are within a person's own control. We have already dealt, for instance, with education and training and willingness and ability (or otherwise) to move. And there are other rather intangible factors such as personality and health.

But the ability to do a job and all that this implies does not necessarily lead to an appointment or promotion. There are other factors which have a bearing on a candidate's chances which are largely outside his control. We are not going to try to list all of these. We shall confine ourselves to a discussion of the following five and of their effects on administrative and clerical staff in the hospital service:

1. *The grading structure* It will be apparent that however many able and otherwise qualified staff there may be at, say, the penultimate level of promotion their chances of further advancement are strictly limited by the number of jobs at the top. Similar considerations apply at every level in the grading structure.

2. *Special developments in the hospital service* The prospects of appointment in the hospital service and promotion prospects for existing staff may improve if some special development leads to an increase in establishments or the upgrading of posts. A current example of this is the expansion of staff which is taking place in many Regional Boards to deal with the Hospital Plan. The recent formation of work study teams is another instance of the kind of thing we have in mind. If appointments for such purposes are made from within the Service these special developments do enhance staffs' career prospects. The converse applies in the event of a decrease in establishments. We have already referred (page 32) to the difficulty of making allowances for special developments of this kind and to our decision to confine ourselves to giving estimates which hospital authorities can add to or subtract from according to their own interpretation of the possible effects of such developments.

3. *Sex* Both from the evidence of our statistics and from our personal experience as hospital administrators, we would say that career prospects in hospital administration are at present less favourable for women than they are for men.

4. *Age* It is only in the clerical grades that salaries are on a wage-for-age basis. But at all levels, age (especially if it carries with it appropriate experience) enters into consideration affecting appointment or promotion. Thus career prospects, as much as recruitment needs with which we have already dealt, may be improved or lessened for staff at particular age levels according to the character of the age structure and its relationship in shape and time to the salary or grading structure.

5. *Promotion ages* There is a particular aspect of the effect of age on career prospects which we find is not widely understood in the hospital service. This is why we are dealing with it under a separate heading. We refer to the age-levels at which hospital authorities have hitherto promoted staff from one grade to another. We shall call these 'promotion ages'.

We do not propose to become involved in the difficult question of the extent to which sex affects a candidate's appointment or promotion prospects. We are aware that the suitability of hospital administration as a career for women is a subject on which opinions are divided. But in contemplating the information contained in our survey we feel that notwithstanding these divided opinions the hospital service should look closely to see if it is making the best possible use of the talent which may be available to it among 'career-minded' women in the administrative and clerical staff. In this matter, as in others, it is important that hospital authorities should take account of the broad social trends in which they have to operate.

The relationship of the grading structure to promotion ages and the effect of this relationship on the staffs' career prospects is also a difficult question, but we shall endeavour to deal with it as simply as possible.

The number of full-time administrative and clerical posts (excluding typists and machine operators) in the hospital service at 31st December 1960[38] was:

Designated and Administrative grades	5,712
Higher Clerical and Clerical	19,808

We estimate that the division of these between men and women was as follows:

	Men	Women
Designated and Administrative grades	5,367	345
Higher Clerical and Clerical	5,912	13,896

It is practically impossible to discuss the career prospects of the 13,896 female clerical staff because of the extent to which their intentions are affected by marriage and motherhood. In the comments which follow we confine our observations to the prospects of the designated and administrative grades (men and women combined) and of the men in the clerical grades.

In common with all others the career prospects of these staff, as we pointed out above, have been affected by the age-levels at which the employing authorities have hitherto promoted them from one grade to another. It will be seen in Appendices 8 and 9 that there is a wide range in the ages at which staff were appointed or promoted to their present grade. If, for the purposes of this discussion, we take the median of the ages at which existing staff were promoted to their present grade and call this the promotion age to that grade, we get the following result:

Promotion age:

to Designated grades (D3)	38
to the Senior Administrative grade	37
to the General Administrative grade	34

For the male clerical staff the promotion age to the Higher Clerical grade has been 31 and the median age of entrants to the Clerical grade in the past has been 24.

At this point, if we were to present a complete picture, our calculations would become very intricate because of the great diversity of ages at which staff have entered the hospital service. In order to simplify the matter and to illustrate the importance of promotion ages we shall assume an approximately even age structure, in which case the annual intake of staff to maintain a total labour force of 11,624 (i.e. 5,712 in the Designated and Administrative grades and 5,912 male clerical staff) would be of the order of 283, i.e. 11,624 divided by 41 (the working span with the present median age at entry of 24).

Now with the existing grading structure and the pattern of promotion ages to which we have already referred, i.e.

Grading structure	No. of Posts	Promotion ages
Designated grades	1,813	38
Senior Administrative	1,149	37
General Administrative	2,750	34
Higher Clerical (male)	3,330	31
Clerical (male)	2,582	24 (Median age at entry)

we can calculate the career prospects of 283 annual entrants. In Appendix 45 we describe in detail how this is done. Briefly, we have taken the number of designated posts and divided these by the 'normal' working-span in these posts. The resultant quotient is the number of staff who (given an even age structure) will obtain designated posts each year. Similar calculation can be made for each grade after a deduction has been made in each grade for those who are passing through it on their way to the grade above.

The result of our calculations is as follows:

67 (24%) would become Designated Officers
39 (14%) would go no higher than the Senior Administrative grade
78 (27%) no higher than the General Administrative grade
$\overline{(65\%)}$
82 (29%) no higher than the Higher Clerical grade
17 (6%) would remain on the Clerical grade.

In presenting these figures we must ask the reader to bear in mind the qualifications and assumptions which underlie our calculations. We are satisfied, however, that these percentages broadly represent the career prospects of the majority of existing staff in terms of statistical probabilities. If anything, a more precise calculation, if it could be made, would perhaps disclose a rather less favourable pattern.

It has been suggested to us by several senior hospital administrators that career prospects for staff would be improved if the promotion ages to the Senior and General Administrative grades and to Higher Clerical posts were respectively 30, 25 and 23 and not as they are in the figures given above 37, 34 and 31. We do not disagree with the suggestion that these would be more appropriate promotion ages for the grades referred to. It is important, however, that the suggestion should be considered in the light of all its practical implications. We mention it here so that we can illustrate the effect of this suggestion if adopted without other changes in the staff structure.

On the same assumptions as we made before, but with these suggested promotion ages and also assuming that in circumstances less abnormal than those of the past twenty years the majority of staff would usually enter the hospital service between the ages of 17 and 23 (i.e. at an average age of, say, 20), the following results would occur: to maintain the labour force there would need to be an annual intake of about 258; the career prospects of these 258 annual entrants with the revised promotion ages and entry age referred to above would be:

67 (26%) would become Designated Officers
18 (7%) would go no higher than the Senior Administrative grade
58 (22%) no higher than the General Administrative grade
‾‾‾‾‾‾
(55%)
72 (28%) no higher than the Higher Clerical grade
43 (17%) would remain on the Clerical grade.

Compare the above percentages with those shown on page 68, in particular the sub-total of 55% with the previous sub-total of 65%. This example illustrates clearly what is in any case fairly obvious, i.e. that the earlier staff reach a grade or the longer the period they spend in it, the smaller the number of people that can hold that grade within a fixed establishment.

The salary range of Designated Officers is very wide and as we have explained in our notes on 'Definitions' (page vi) we divided this into three categories:

		Minimum Salaries
D.1	—	£2,000 +
D.2	—	£1,500 to £1,999
D.3	—	Less than £1,500

Of the 67 staff who can expect to become Designated Officers their prospects with respect to these categories are:

5 to D.1 (median age of promotion 43)
26 to D.2 (median age of promotion 40)
36 to D.3 (median age of promotion 38)

The foregoing calculations relate to the position in the hospital service as it now is. Some consideration must therefore be given to the fact that at present not all promotion roads lead to the 'top'. As we have already noted, the service is fragmented in relation to the appointment and promotion of administrative and clerical staff by the existence of 429 autonomous employing authorities. Within this fragmented structure there exist (to repeat Noel Hall's phrase) the 'little worlds' of hospital administration, three main divisions of which are General Management, Finance administration and Supplies administration. There are other little worlds such as Medical Records and, more recently, Work Study, not to mention Medical administration and Nursing administration. In this country (cf. for example the USA and Australia) neither of the last two mentioned is considered part of the broad stream of hospital administration. As experience in industry and other forms of public service shows, the confluence of various tributaries of functional administration into the broad stream of general management is difficult but not impossible. In our view the hospital service should move towards such an objective. In the past the promotion prospects of a new entrant were normally restricted to the confines of the particular division of administration into which he was recruited. This obviously had a limiting effect on an individual's career prospects.

This condition is being rectified, particularly in areas where there are schemes of post-entry training, but movement from one division of administration to another is still by no means easily achieved and for that matter there are special problems in providing for movement particularly in the middle grades of the Service.

It is possible to distinguish the number of designated posts falling

Table 33 *Distribution of Staff in Divisions of Administration*

Division	Men		Women		Total	
	No.	*% of total*	*No.*	*% of total*	*No.*	*% of total*
General Management	649	38·9	303	24·8	952	32·9
Finance . . .	590	35·4	170	13·9	760	26·2
Supplies . .	161	9·7	23	1·9	184	6·4
Medical Records .	95	5·7	565	46·2	660	22·8
Medical Administration	11	·7	23	1·9	34	1·2
Architects/Engineers	32	1·9	17	1·4	49	1·7
Stores . . .	61	3·6	8	·6	69	2·4
Establishments .	15	·9	5	·4	20	·7
Other . . .	54	3·2	109	8·9	163	5·7
Total . .	1,668	100	1,223	100	2,891	100
Not stated . .	58		133		191	
	1,726		1,356		3,082	

into the three main divisions of General Management, Finance and Supplies, but below the designated grades the distinction becomes increasingly difficult as one goes down from the Senior Administrative grade to the Clerical grade. This difficulty arises because some of the junior posts necessitate a combination of functions. Nevertheless we believe we have been able to make the distinctions with a fair measure of accuracy for the staff in our survey group. The resultant analysis is contained in Appendix 13 (men) and Appendix 14 (women) and is summarized in Table 33.

In order to estimate the effect of these divisions in the administration on our preceding calculations of career prospects we have made the following further analysis. The percentage of the administrative grades and of the male clerical staff engaged in General Management (including Establishments), Finance and Supplies (including Stores) is given in Table 34.

Table 34 *Percentage of Administrative Grades and Male Clerical Staff by Divisions of Administration*

Division	SA	GA	HC	C
General Management	53·5	39·6	31·9	25·7
Finance . . .	24·5	35·6	44·0	30·9
Supplies . . .	10·5	10·3	8·9	27·1
Other . . .	11·5	14·5	15·2	16·3

These proportions applied to the national totals in the administrative grades and the male clerical grades give the following estimates of staff

Table 35 *Estimated Numbers of Staff in Designated and Administrative and Male Clerical Grades by Divisions of Administration England and Wales*

Division	D	SA	GA	HC	C	Total
General Management	1,002	614	1,088	1,063	664	4,440
Finance . .	534	282	980	1,464	798	4,081
Supplies . .	258	121	283	296	699	1,595
Other . . .	19	132	399	507	421	1,508
	1,813	1,149	2,750	3,330	2,582	11,624

(Table 35) in each division of administration in these grades. To these estimates we have added the numbers of designated officers according to their administrative function.

If the promotion ages to which we referred on page 68 are applied to each of these divisions of administration then the career prospects of the 258 annual entrants with respect to these divisions would be those shown in Table 36.

Table 36 *Career Prospects of Staff by Divisions of Administration*

Grade	General Management	Finance	Supplies	Other	Total
To DO	37	20	9	0·7	67
SA	9	4	1	4	18
GA	21	22	6	9	58
HC	22	32	6	12	72
C	9	13	14	7	43
Total	98	91	36	33	258
Above totals as % of 258	38	35	14	13	100

From Table 36 it would seem that of the 258 annual entrants who, given an even age distribution, would be necessary to maintain the total labour force of designated and administrative grades and male clerical staff, with the existing grading structure and entry at about 20 years of age, 98 would be needed for General Management, 91 for Finance and 36 for Supplies and the chances of these attaining designated posts would be 37, 20 and 9 respectively.

We have taken this 'norm' of 258 annual entrants in order to have a point of reference for our calculations and observations. It will be evident that the career prospects of particular groups of staff will vary from group to group, and also for each group from time to time according to conditions which are outside our power to calculate or predict.

The prospects hitherto open to the majority of staff in which approximately one-quarter could expect to become Designated Officers, two-fifths to remain in the middle-grades and one-third in the clerical grades, seem to correspond roughly to the present promotion-expectations of staff (except, as would be expected, there are not sufficient designated posts for all who would wish to have one) and also to the existing pattern of education and training and staffs' willingness and ability to move which we have described in the preceding chapters.

This is not to say that we view the present conditions as satisfactory. We shall be suggesting in our Epilogue how we think these can be improved.

Chapter 8 Conclusions

The page numbers in the margin refer to observations made in the
preceding Chapters and in the Epilogue

Staff Records

In our view it is important for the proper conduct of the hospital
service that there should be some readily available staff records (the
basic statistics at least) of *all* the administrative and clerical staff in the
employment of the hospital authorities. These should be sufficiently
detailed to enable distinctions to be made by grades and sex and, if
possible, by age. The records should be maintained by the Boards and
collated nationally. Such records are indispensable, for instance, to
calculations of the Service's recruitment needs. A considerable amount
of information is undoubtedly available in the records of the Ministry
of Health's Superannuation Division but not, apparently, in a form
that makes it readily accessible for calculations relating to a specific
section of hospital staff.

Quite a lot could be done with a minimum amount of change if the
Ministry of Health amended their forms SH6 and SH7. Up to and
including 1960, these distinguished the numbers for male and female
clerical staff. In 1961 the form no longer called for separate figures.
This change should be reversed and the forms should be revised so that
the distinction between male and female staff is made for all grades of
staff. No great additional labour would be involved in the completion
of the forms if they were also revised to show for each authority:—

The number of staff by grade and sex who, since the previous year's
return, have:—

(*a*) Left   i The hospital service

           or ii To go to another hospital authority

(*b*) Joined   i From another hospital authority

           or ii From outside the hospital service

These particulars alone would provide useful data on recruitment
needs, labour turnover and movement in and out of the hospital service.
They could be obtained with comparatively small adjustments to the
annual returns. Furthermore these changes could, we believe, be made
quite quickly and with the agreement of the hospital authorities.

Ideally the annual returns should supply information that would
give a complete account of the existing age structures and make it

74

p. 1

p.2

p. 18

possible for changes in these to be traced from year to year. It would p. 40 not be as easy to do this as to make the revisions we have already suggested. But consideration should be given to this possibility, if it can be achieved without much additional effort, because particulars relating to the age structures are of prime importance to estimates of recruitment needs and career prospects. If an annual return is not possible these particulars should be obtained at intervals of no more than five years.

If there is to be a satisfactory career structure the collection of information of the kind we have suggested is of equal importance to staff as it is to management.*

Age Structures pp. 6–31

From our experience in this survey and from our discussions with staff managers in organizations which offer comparable forms of employment, we have concluded that statistics about the age structures for both sexes and for each grade of staff are important prerequisites for the formulation of a recruitment policy.

Recruitment Policy pp. 32–41

In our view the time has come when the hospital service should have p. 37 a planned recruitment policy. This is necessary if the Service is to meet p. 31 the needs and attain the objectives referred to in Chapter 4.

One of the objects of the policy should be to secure a more even distribution of male administrative and clerical staff over the whole age-range of 16 to 65. In consultation with the staff associations, p. 39 representatives of the employing authorities should consider how this could be achieved during the next ten years. Only in exceptional circumstances should men enter the Service in those age-groups in p. 40 which there are disproportionately large numbers of male staff and every effort should be made to recruit men in appropriate numbers at each p. 40 age in the lower age-groups in which there are deficiencies.

---

* In June 1962 the Ministry of Health requested hospital Boards and Committees to make a return of all staff in the designated and administrative grades. The form used (SBH100) called for details about age, sex, grading, education, etc. These details are being collected for the information of the Lycett Green Committee which has been set up to consider the administrative and clerical staffing arrangements in the hospital service.[39]

Compared with the annual recruitment of 258* required under the assumptions referred to in Chapter 4, the Service will need less than this number during the next ten years and thereafter increasingly more throughout the period 1971 to 1985. Since current recruitment should have regard to the long-term needs of the Service, special thought will have to be given as to how at a time when the number of retirals will be less than the 'norm' of 258 it may be necessary to recruit more than this number to ensure an adequacy of staff at the right age and with the right experience to meet the large number of retirals which will occur after 1971.

p. 39

The difficulties which result from the 'excess' of men in the age-range of 31–55 (in ten years' time 41–65) might be eased if some of the staff in the upper part of this age-range were offered and accepted the prospect of early retirement on favourable terms. This might be facilitated if the superannuation regulations were revised.†

p. 39

pp. 65–73 Recruitment should be related to the staffs' career prospects and should differentiate between the administrative and clerical needs of the Service. It is, perhaps, also desirable to acknowledge that there pp. 81–82 are jobs and staff which are neither administrative nor clerical but executive, in the Civil Service sense of these terms.

The recruitment policy should be under constant review to anticipate :—

pp. 32–33 (a) changes in the hospital service (e.g. developments resulting from the current Capital Development Programme; the application of automation especially in Finance and Supplies); and

(b) changes in social and economic trends in our society.

pp. 28–30 *Adjustment to Social Trends*

The tardiness with which hospital authorities have adjusted themselves to post-war trends has contributed to the failure of the Service to recruit young men in adequate numbers for administrative and clerical work. The fact that the salaries which can be offered, for example, at ages 16, pp. 26–28 18 and 21 are less than in comparable forms of employment must place the hospital service at some disadvantage in a highly competitive market. But experience has shown that even this disadvantage can be overcome if hospital authorities 'set out their stall' and are in the market

---

* An addition will have to be made to this figure to allow for wastage (page 33).
† Since this was written, a Ministry circular HM(62)49 published in August 1962 records some revision of the superannuation regulations.

at the right time of the year. This can best be achieved if authorities pp. 29-30 pool their needs and have a form of consolidated advertising in anticipation of the end of the school year. This has been done in some areas recently but it still by no means a common practice. An exception to this generalization is the arrangements which now exist for the annual recruitment of entrants to the Junior Administrative grade. p. 2

Of the social changes which have affected recruitment since the war pp. 28-29 insufficient account has been taken of the effects of full employment, the 1944 Education Act and the drift from white to blue-collar and white-coated employment and from liberal arts subjects to science and technology. Other developments which should be allowed for in the proposed recruitment policy are the changing attitudes to the employment of married women and mothers and the current phenomenon of the 'vanishing spinster'.[40]

Female Staff

This leads us to comment again on our conclusion that hospital pp. 66 Boards and Committees should consider whether they are making the best use of talent available to them among both the career-minded women and other female staff. At present there are not many of the pp. 63-64 former but this may reflect the fact that for women the chances of promotion out of the clerical grades seem to have been very few in the past.

We would not restrict prospects for female staff to any particular sections of administrative or clerical work but there are undoubtedly some posts for which they are particularly suited.

Finance Staff

Special consideration will also have to be given to the needs and pp. 60 future of finance administration. The Service is not itself producing many qualified accountants. The extent to which these are necessary is a matter on which there is no commonly accepted view in the hospital service. The experience of the National Selection Committee shows that only about 1 in 50 of the direct entrants to the Junior Administrative grade is interested in training for a career in finance administration.

Selection Process

A conclusion which does not emerge directly from our survey but which has impressed itself upon us during our research and during our discussions with the staff managers of organizations offering comparable forms of employment, is the outstanding importance of the selection process. A planned recruitment policy may attract suitable applicants in adequate numbers. The importance then of choosing from among these applicants those who are best suited can hardly be exaggerated. This is especially critical in the initial selection of those who may later obtain promotion to administrative posts.

The importance of the selection process relates not only to recruits but also to existing staff seeking entry into and advancement within the administrative grades.

pp. 42–55 *Mobility*

Selection for promotion should be linked with arrangements designed p. 52 to secure the movement of staff who wish to move in order to extend their experience. In our view there should be a considerable degree of mobility in the Junior Administrative grade and a fair measure of pp. 46–47 mobility in the General Administrative grade. The former is the basic training grade and the movement of trainees in this is now ensured by the National and Regional Training Schemes. The General Administrative grade should be regarded as an advanced training grade approximately equivalent to the first five years of post-registration p. 45 training received by a young doctor. In future this grade should be for staff at ages of about 25 to 30. During this period a member of staff should have experience with at least two different authorities in addition to those with which he received his basic training. There should be some p. 47 financial incentive and payment of removal expenses to encourage a p. 44 person to move while remaining in this grade; 64% of the men now in the General Administrative grade have made no move since 1948, p. 43 although 75% to 90% have attempted to move. The reasons for this are clear from the data given in Chapter 5, in which we concluded that the p. 44 present position is not satisfactory for a service in which, because of its fragmentary nature, administrative staff usually have to make a number of moves to gain promotion and a diversity of experience.

Training pp. 56–64

As a corollary to this we also conclude that while the basic training arrangements now coming into effect for the Junior Administrative grade are adequate, the advanced education and training of staff in the administrative grades leaves much to be desired. This conclusion is supported, we think, by the facts given in Chapter 6.

In our view it is time that the 'Robinson Crusoe' attitude to training was supplemented by organized arrangements. p. 61

Career Prospects pp. 65–73

Our conclusions from the calculations we made of staffs' career prospects are that there is a rough correlation between these prospects and their career expectations (except, of course, that there are not sufficient designated posts for all who would wish to have one) and their education, training and mobility.

General Conclusion

There is one general conclusion which we think is inescapable.

If there is to be a planned recruitment policy which will take account of the ever-changing conditions both within and outside the Service and if this is to be supplemented by satisfactory arrangements for staff selection, movement, training and promotion, then it is no longer possible to leave so much to the unguided and often uninformed activities of pp. 37–38 429 separate hospital authorities.

In our view the work of the Regional Staff Advisory Committees should be extended and co-ordinated nationally by a Hospital Service Commission. The Commission should be responsible for the statistical records for all fourteen regions and Wales. The information for each region should be known to the Staff Advisory Committee for that region p. 74 but calculations, for instance, of recruitment needs must be made in relation to the figures for England and Wales as a whole since each region is not a self-contained entity and nothing should be done to preclude movement between the regions.

Throughout this report we have assumed a continuance of the existing grading structure. In the course of our work on the survey during the past two and a half years we have come to the conclusion that there might be benefit to both management and staff if the present structure were re-formed. In the following Epilogue we submit some pp. 80–83 suggestions as to what might be done.

Epilogue

In view of the changes that have been made in the administrative and clerical staff grading system from time to time since 1948 we hesitate to suggest yet another change. We do so, however, because in our submission, the changes of the past have been adjustments rather than major reforms of the structure and because we feel that if any major reform is to be made then this is about the right time to make it. The hospital service has now had fourteen years' experience of the present arrangements. This seems to be sufficiently long as a testing period and yet not too long for the system to become inextricably deep-rooted. It is probably true now that if a major change is necessary the sooner it is made the better.

In our view, a re-organization along the lines which we are about to propose would bring the administrative and clerical staff structure more into accord with the conditions of the Service as they now exist, and it would enable recruitment, selection, training and movement to be related to the kind of jobs the staff will be required to do or to which they aspire.

During the later stages of our survey we became increasingly impressed by the extent to which the administrative and clerical staff fall into *three* broad groups and we would suggest that there should be a re-organization of the Service along the lines of (though not necessarily identical with) the Civil Service, i.e. there should be three branches—the administrative, the executive and the clerical. Each of these branches should in itself provide a satisfactory career for those in it and there should be every possibility of transfer from one branch to another.

In our interpretation of how the three Branches would operate there is no idea of changing the responsibilities of committees under the 1946 Act. It seems to us that there is nothing irreconcilable between a reformed staffing structure and the retention of voluntary committees and their power to appoint their chief officers. Indeed, in our view, there is a special relationship between Boards and Committees and their chief officers which would be lost if the voluntary members were not able to choose the chief officers with whom they have to work. This could be done just as effectively, perhaps more effectively, from a cadre of administrative staff whose initial selection and subsequent training had been the subject of special care.

Posts in the administrative branch would lead to positions of chief and deputy chief administrative officer; in the executive branch to a chief executive grade and in the clerical branch to "senior clerical officer". The method of assimilating the present grading structure to a new structure of this kind would, of course, be a rather complicated process and would have to be a matter for negotiation and agreement between the management side and the staff associations on the Administrative and Clerical Staffs Whitley Council. There should in any event be an understanding about 'no detriment' to safeguard the personal position of existing staff. The details of this would need close consideration. We have given some thought to this and we are satisfied that the change could be made at no great cost to the Service.

There is a view that 'administration' in some conventionally accepted sense of the term is not, in general, a responsibility of senior staff in the hospital service. This view is reflected in the following observation contained in Sir Noel Hall's report. He said 'If the word "administrative" had not come into common use in the hospital service, I should not have used it, save at very few points . . . because a great deal of the work which is called administrative in the hospital service would not be so-called elsewhere'.[41]

If it is intended that administration should imply 'policy formation' and 'decision-making' then, in our view, there is, or ought to be, sufficient of this in the hands of the chief officers of Boards and Committees to justify its application to their functions. The contrary view is presumably derived from a belief that the 'real administration' is performed by the hospital Boards and Committees themselves and not by their senior staff. Undoubtedly the position varies from authority to authority. A great deal depends upon the personality of the authorities' chief officers.

We have found that many senior hospital officers agree with Sir Noel Hall's view that the term 'administrative' is at present too widely applied in the hospital service. Even within the designated grades there are a considerable number of posts which do not involve any real measure of policy formation and decision-making. But by no means can all posts which are not administrative be classified as 'clerical'. It is apparent from the saving clause in Sir Noel Hall's observation that his views and those of many senior hospital officers are fairly close and that the only issue to be decided is—at how many points can the term 'administrative' be applied to the responsibilities of senior hospital service staff?

The extent to which the term 'administrative' is more widely used in the hospital service compared, for example, with the Civil Service is revealed by these figures: the number of permanent Administrative, Executive and Clerical staff in the Civil Service (1st January 1962) is 236,800. Of these, 3,199 (1·3%) are in the Administrative class.[42] In the hospital service with a total of 32,211 administrative and clerical staff, 5,712 (17·7%) are in the designated and administrative grades.

The problem is, of course, largely one of definition but it is of some importance for the hospital service to relate its definitions to one of the commonly accepted ways in which 'administrative' and 'clerical' are used.

One of the first requirements before any changes could be made would be a decision on the number of posts or staff to be placed in the chief or deputy chief administrative grade. So that this decision could be reached as objectively as possible all existing designated officers should be given the administrative grading on a 'protected' basis. The classification of their posts as 'Administrative' or 'Executive' would not then be affected by personal considerations.

When a decision has been reached about the number of positions at the top and next to the top of the administrative branch, it will be possible to calculate how many annual recruits there should be to the Junior Administrative grade and how many posts there should be in the intermediate administrative grades.

We are reluctant to suggest any numbers because this should be done only after careful assessment of the work content of all posts. There is also the risk if we attach numbers to the proposed three branches that arguments over the validity or otherwise of the numbers will obscure the discussion of general principles.

We cannot, however, talk about recruitment needs relevant to a structure composed of three branches without offering some suggestions about the numbers in each branch so we shall do this in round terms. These should not be taken as anything other than broad indications of the possible effects of a re-organization.

The number of posts in the administrative branch would probably be rather more than 1,000 and in the executive branch about 5,000. The clerical branch should have two divisions—division A for career clerical staff and division B for clerks (chiefly short-stay staff) who have no career ambitions. In the first of these two divisions there would be about 6,300 posts and in division B about 13,300.

With these numbers and on the assumption of an even age structure, the annual intake, apart from transfers, into the three branches would need to be:—

27 into the Junior Administrative grade;

232 into the clerical branch Division A;
> of these about 115 would transfer in their early twenties to the Executive branch each year.

We could only estimate the annual intake into the clerical division **B** if information was available on the labour turnover of non-career clerical staff.

If the average length of service of such staff is, for instance, five years then the annual intake would be of the order of 2,660.

To all of these figures except the last an addition—possibly 20%—would have to be made to allow for wastage. At first sight it might seem that our proposals will add more complications to the already complicated system of salary computation (e.g. the 'pointing' system which determines the salaries of designated officers). We have carefully considered this risk which should certainly be avoided. We are satisfied that within the framework of our proposals it would be possible, if anything, for the position to be somewhat simplified without any detriment to staff.

An important result of the changes we are suggesting would be a clearer definition of staffs' responsibilities, and this would facilitate the processes of recruitment, selection, basic training and movement associated with advanced training. These processes could be more closely related to staffs' aspirations and their potential.

Since the quality of administration is largely determined by the selection and training of administrators the proposals we have made would, we believe, help the hospital service to achieve a high standard of administration.

References

Ref. No.	Page No.	Reference
1	1	These numbers relate to the position as it was at the time of the Survey. Details for each region are given in Appendix 2iii.
2	1	A brief description of the changes brought about by nationalization of the hospital service in 1948 can be found in the booklet 'Hospitals and the State—Background and Blueprint'. The Acton Society Trust, 1955.
3	1	Report of Ministry of Health for the year ended 31st December 1960. (Cmnd. 1418) H.M.S.O. Tables J, N, O, P and Q, pages 185–201.
4	1	*Ibid.*, page 7.
5	2	This figure is calculated from the 1962 Hospitals Year Book, i.e. it is the number of Hospital Management Committees at the time of the Survey.
6	2	Ministry of Health Memorandum HM(56)32.
7	2	Ministry of Health Memorandum HM(61)117.
8	2	Report on the Grading Structure of Administrative and Clerical Staff in the Hospital Service (The 'Noel Hall' Report). H.M.S.O. 1957, paras. 12–22.
9	2	*Ibid.*, para. 85.
10	3	Since this was written the Welsh Hospital Board have completed a survey of administrative and clerical staff in Wales. By arrangement with us this survey was identical with ours. Thus, the Welsh Board now has much of this information for most (although still not all) of the staff in their area.
11	3	Speaking of the response to mail surveys of the general population, C. A. Moser (*Survey Methods in Social Investigation*, Wm. Heinemann Ltd., 1958, page 179) says: 'Strenuous efforts are usually needed to bring the response rate above about 30 or 40%'.
12	3	Appendix 2i gives some details of the staff grading structure and salary rates.
13	5	Report on a Survey. Administrative and Clerical Staffs in Hospitals in Wales, 1960–61. Anne Crichton. Published by Welsh Staff Advisory Committee. Welsh Hospital Board. 1962.
14	9	Part I 1951 Census Report, Table ii.3.
15	26	Clegg and Chester, *Wage Policy and the Health Service*, Blackwells, 1956, page 170.
16	26	*Ibid.*, page 117.
17	28	Royal Commission on the Civil Service, Minutes of Evidence, Twenty-first Day, November 8th, 1954. (Quoted by Clegg and Chester, *Ibid.*, pages 79 and 80.)
18	29	Political and Economic Planning, *Graduate Employment*, George Allen and Unwin, September 1956, page 95. See also the whole of Chapter III, 'The Choice of a Career', in this work.
19	29	Nigel Walker, *Morale in the Civil Service*. Edinburgh University Press, 1961, page 3.
20	29	R. P. Harper, 'The Recruitment of School Leavers into Hospital Administration', THE HOSPITAL, September 1961. Vol. 57, No. 9, page 571.
21	30	Private communication, 27th July 1962.
22	30	Ministry of Health Memorandum HM(56)32.
23	30	Ministry of Health Memorandum HM(61)117.
24	31	R. C. Millward, 'The Administrative and Clerical Establishment in a Hospital Group', THE HOSPITAL, May 1951. Vol. 47, No. 5, pages 309–314.

Ref. No.	Page No.	Reference
25	32	A Hospital Plan for England and Wales (Cmnd. 1604). H.M.S.O· January 1962.
26	38	There are fifteen Regional Boards; thirty-six Boards of Governors and 378 Hospital Management Committees.
27	40	There may be some expansion, for example, in connection with the Capital Development Programme (the 'Hospital Plan for England and Wales', *Ibid.*).
28	41	The chief amendments have been the change from the original grading to 'lettered grades' in 1951 and the change from these to the 'named grades' in 1958.
29	41	These were RHB(47)1 dated June 1947; BG(48)1 and HMC(48)2. The first two specified the administrative and clerical staffing for Regional Boards and Boards of Governors. HMC(48)2 dealt with the staff for Hospital Management Committees and (non-teaching) hospital units.
30	41	There have been two exceptions to this generalization. These are the arrangements under the National Training Scheme and the new Regional Training Scheme. See page 40.
31	42	Strictly speaking, the Boards only are the 'employers' (i.e. in law) but in fact the 378 Hospital Management Committees also appoint and dismiss their administrative and clerical staff.
32	48	In this paragraph we have used 'senior designated post' to mean a Chief Officer's post and the term 'junior designated post' to mean a designated post other than one held by a Chief Officer.
33	56	R. J. Pitt, 'The National Training Scheme', THE HOSPITAL, February 1961. Vol. 57, No. 2, pages 89–93. R. E. Jefford and others. 'The National Training Scheme', *Ibid.*, March 1961. Vol. 57, No. 3, pages 146–8. V. F. Driscoll. 'Training for Hospital Administration', *Ibid.*, September 1961. Vol. 57, No. 9, pages 573–5. Editorial in THE HOSPITAL, 'Progress in Training', September 1961. Vol. 57, No. 9, pages 557–9.
34	56	THE HOSPITAL, September 1960. Vol. 56, No. 9, pages 759–67.
35	58	Memorandum of the Council of the Institute of Hospital Administrators, reprinted in THE HOSPITAL, May 1960. Vol. 56, No. 5, pages 385–8.
36	60	See, for example, Addendum to HMC(48)2. August 1948.
37	60	Professor Roy Sidebotham, *Hospital Service Finance Staffs*. Published by the Association of Chief Financial Officers in the Hospital Service in England and Wales.
38	66	See Appendix 2ii.
39	75	For terms of reference and membership, see page 128, THE HOSPITAL, February 1962. Vol 55, No. 2.
40	77	See 'Women Talking' by Mary Scott (*Guardian*, 10th September 1962, page 6) and the article to which she refers, 'Growth Productivity and Womanpower' by Professor T. E. Chester, in the District Bank 'Review', September 1962. No. 143, pages 18–35.
41	81	*Op cit.*, para 23.
42	82	This information was supplied by H.M. Treasury.

Appendix 1

THE UNIVERSITY OF LEEDS

Hospital Service Administrative Staff Research Project

Department of Adult Education,
The University,
Leeds 2.

Telephone: Leeds 31751.

Director: J. Griffith, B.Litt., M.A., F.H.A.
Assistant: E. T. Rees, B.A., D.S.A.

The Nuffield Provincial Hospitals Trust have asked the University to extend a survey that I have been making of the Administrative and Clerical staff of the Hospital Service.

So far the survey has been confined to the 'middle-grades' in the Sheffield and Liverpool Regions. With your co-operation, we now hope to extend the survey. First, we would like to include the senior and junior administrative staff in the Sheffield and Liverpool Regions and also to bring our previous information on the 'middle-grades' up to date. Secondly, we want to include the administrative staff of the North-East Metropolitan and South Western Regions in the extended survey.

The main objectives of the survey are to make some assessment:

(*a*) of the promotion chances and prospects of movement which the Hospital Service has to offer its administrative and clerical staff;

(*b*) of the training needs of those in the service;

(*c*) of the annual recruitment needs into the junior grades for the next ten years.

Experience in other organizations has shown that the making of such assessments with any degree of accuracy calls for a considerable amount of information and co-operation from the staff concerned.

Thus I am writing to ask whether you would consider letting me have the personal particulars set out on the accompanying form. These details will be treated as *strictly confidential.* Under no circumstances will they be available to anyone outside the University. Some of the questions are obviously of an intimate nature, *e.g.* those relating to housing, number of children, employment and educational background. But they are all relevant to the objects of our enquiry. I do hope you will not regard them as an unwarranted encroachment on your privacy.

I should like to make two points quite clear. This survey is entirely independent of any action which might have been taken by Regional Hospital Boards as a result of the issue of H.M.(59)59 (Promotion and Appointments Procedures for Administrative Staff). Its purpose is NOT to provide a central register to which hospital authorities might turn when about to appoint administrative staff.

Our intention is to obtain a general picture of the Administrative and Clerical staff structure so that we are able to consider what the future has in store both for the individual and the Hospital Service as a whole.

If you are willing to help please complete our form and send it back in the reply-paid envelope as soon as possible. Do not sign the form.

In return for your help we will let you know the generalized results of this survey and any proposals that emerge from it.

JOHN GRIFFITH
Director.

The University of Leeds

Survey of Administrative and Clerical Staff of the Hospital Service

Jobs (including War or National Service), since completion of full-time education *Present post last*

DATE (approx.)		EMPLOYER	POST HELD	IF N.H.S.	
From	To			Dept.	Grade*

*Please state actual grade (e.g., Hospital Secretary 10½-20 points; General Administrative Grade; Clerical Grade, etc.)

Where present post is with Board of Governors or H.M.C.—*please indicate with* ✔

If wholly employed at a hospital ☐

If wholly employed at group offices ☐

If other (please specify below)* ☐

*.. 1 - 2

Age full-time education completed ☐

For University use only

3	4	5	6	7	8	9	10	11	12	13	14	15	16	17	18	19	20	21	22
0	0	0	0	0	0	0	0	0	0	0	0	0	0	0	0	0	0	0	0
1	1	1	1	1	1	1	1	1	1	1	1	1	1	1	1	1	1	1	1
2	2	2	2	2	2	2	2	2	2	2	2	2	2	2	2	2	2	2	2
3	3	3	3	3	3	3	3	3	3	3	3	3	3	3	3	3	3	3	3
4	4	4	4	4	4	4	4	4	4	4	4	4	4	4	4	4	4	4	4
5	5	5	5	5	5	5	5	5	5	5	5	5	5	5	5	5	5	5	5
6	6	6	6	6	6	6	6	6	6	6	6	6	6	6	6	6	6	6	6
7	7	7	7	7	7	7	7	7	7	7	7	7	7	7	7	7	7	7	7
8	8	8	8	8	8	8	8	8	8	8	8	8	8	8	8	8	8	8	8
9	9	9	9	9	9	9	9	9	9	9	9	9	9	9	9	9	9	9	9

4. **Present annual salary** £ [23—26]

5. **Sex**—*Indicate with* ✔   27

    Male   1 ☐

    Female   2 ☐

6. **Year of Birth** [28—29]

7. **Anticipated year of retirement** [30—31]

    N.B. Questions 8-13 are concerned with difficulties connected with mobility in the Hospital Service

8. **Marital status**—*Indicate with* ✔   32

    Married   1 ☐

    Single   2 ☐

    Widowed   3 ☐

    Divorced   4 ☐

9. **If married, widowed or divorced please state**—   33—34

    (a) Age at marriage [ ]

    (b) Children   35

        Number in 0-5 yrs. age group ☐

                36

        Number in 6-10 yrs. age group ☐

                37

        Number in 11-15 yrs. age group ☐

                38

        Number in 16+ yrs. age group ☐

                39

        Total of above children ☐

(c) **Is your husband/wife engaged in paid employment?** *Indicate with* ✔   40

    No   1 ☐

    Yes—Full-time   2 ☐

    Yes—Part-time   3 ☐

    Not applicable*   4 ☐

    *i.e. in case of widowed or divorced persons

10. **Housing**—*Indicate with* ✔ *where appropriate*   41

    Buying (or have completed buying) House/Flat   1 ☐

    Renting Council House/Flat   2 ☐

    Renting Private House/Flat   3 ☐

    Living in Lodgings   4 ☐

    Living with parents/relations   5 ☐

    Other (please specify below) *   6 ☐

    * ....

11. **Attempts to move from one Hospital Authority another since July 5th, 1948**

    Approximate number of—   42—43

    (a) Applications submitted [ ]

                    44—45

    (b) Interviews/Short Lists [ ]

                    46—47

    (c) Appointments Obtained [ ]

12. **In contemplating movement have your decision been affected by any of the following factors?**

    If answer is 'yes', indicate with ✔   48

    Housing   1 ☐

    Children's Schooling   2 ☐

    Dependent Relatives   3 ☐

    Lack of Financial Incentive   4 ☐

    Lack of Removal Allowance   5 ☐

    Other Reasons (please specify below) *   6 ☐

    * ....

Would you be prepared to move to ANY part of the country to further your career? *Indicate with √*

49

Yes 1 ☐

No 2 ☐

If the answer is 'No', please specify area/areas which hold no attraction for you—

....

....

What grade do you expect to reach before retirement ? *Indicate with √*

50

Designated Officer (Chief Administrative / Finance / Supplies Officer of an Authority) 1 ☐

Designated Officer (other than above) 2 ☐

Senior Administrative 3 ☐

General Administrative 4 ☐

Higher Clerical (or equivalent) 5 ☐

Clerical (or equivalent) 6 ☐

Education (Full-time)—*Indicate with √ in the appropriate box(es) the nature of your general education*

51

Elementary 1 ☐

Private 2 ☐

Central (Secondary Modern) 3 ☐

Technical/Commercial 4 ☐

Secondary (Grammar) 5 ☐

Public (i.e. a "Headmasters' Conference" School) 6 ☐

University (Full-time only) 7 ☐

Other (please specify below) * 8 ☐

* ....

16. **Education undertaken since working career commenced.** *Indicate with √*

University: 52

Full-time 1 ☐

Part-time 2 ☐

Technical/Commercial College:

Full-time 3 ☐

Part-time 4 ☐

Correspondence Courses 5 ☐

Other (please specify below) * 6 ☐

* ....

17. **Courses and Training Schemes**—*Indicate with √ any of the following courses or schemes in which you have taken part*

53

King's Fund Bursaries or 2-year Course 1 ☐

King's Fund Administrative Staff College Courses 2 ☐

Leeds University Pilot Scheme 3 ☐

National Training Scheme 4 ☐

N.A.L.G.O. Schools, etc. 5 ☐

I.H.A. Schools, etc. 6 ☐

Regional Training Schemes 7 ☐

Board of Governors/H.M.C. Training Schemes 8 ☐

Other (please specify below) * 9 ☐

* ....

18. **Was your education or professional training adversely affected by the War?** *Indicate with √*

54

Yes 1 ☐

No 2 ☐

19. **Examinations**

   (a) **General** – *Indicate with* ✔

      G.C.E. ' O ' level—5 or more subjects (including equivalents—   55

      School Certificate, Matriculation, etc.)   1 ☐

      G.C.E. ' O ' level—less than 5 subjects   2 ☐

      G.C.E. 'A' level (or Higher School Certificate)   3 ☐

      Other examinations of similar standard (please specify below)*   4 ☐

      *..

   (b) **Professional, University, etc., Examinations taken or in prospect**
      (e.g. A.H.A., A.C.I.S., A.I.M.T.A., D.P.A., Degrees, etc.)—*Please specify* —

EXAMINATION	RESULT OF LAST ATTEMPT	DATE OF LAST OR NEXT ATTEMPT

For University Use Only

56	57	58	59	60	61	62	63	64	65
0	0	0	0	0	0	0	0	0	0
1	1	1	1	1	1	1	1	1	1
2	2	2	2	2	2	2	2	2	2
3	3	3	3	3	3	3	3	3	3
4	4	4	4	4	4	4	4	4	4
5	5	5	5	5	5	5	5	5	5
6	6	6	6	6	6	6	6	6	6
7	7	7	7	7	7	7	7	7	7
8	8	8	8	8	8	8	8	8	8
9	9	9	9	9	9	9	9	9	9

20. **Any comments or further information which may be relevant and helpful**

92

Appendix 2.i

Administrative and Clerical Staff Grading Structure

This is not a complete description. Some impression of the complexities of the grading structure can be gained by reference to the Circulars of the NHS Administrative and Clerical Staffs Whitley Council.

Designated Officers

These include the Secretaries and their Deputies of Regional Boards, Boards of Governors and Hospital Management Committees. Not all authorities are large enough to justify 'Deputies'.

Some Boards also have Assistant Secretaries, Principal Administrative Assistants and Legal Advisers.

Senior finance posts: Treasurers and their Deputies (Regional Boards) and Finance Officers in many other authorities.

About 186 (in 414) of the Management Committees and Boards of Governors have Supplies Officers.

Deputy Finance Officers and Deputy Supplies Officers are appointed only in the larger authorities.

Some senior posts are combined, e.g. Group Secretary and Finance Officer or Group Finance and Supplies Officer.

The salaries of most of the above staff are based on a 'group' or 'points' system related to the size of their authority.

Approximately 244 Hospital Secretaries are also paid on the 'points' system and these we have included in the Designated Officers' category in this survey.

Salaries of Designated Officers range from about £1,200 to an ultimate maximum of £3,640 (1961 rates). There are some designated Hospital Secretaries (Boards of Governors) below this range.

There are staff who retain designated titles such as Deputy Group Secretary, Deputy Finance Officer and Hospital Secretary but are, in fact, paid on the general grades referred to below. Throughout the survey these staff were included in the grades on which they are paid.

General Grades

Other grades of staff are usually referred to as General Grades. The main grades are:

Grade	Gross Salary Range (1961 rates)		
Senior Administrative	£1,050	to	£1,290
General Administrative	800	to	1,050
Higher Clerical	620	to	785
Clerical	260 (at 16) to		650
Shorthand Typists and some Machine Operators .	300 (at 16) to		650
Copy Typists and Machine Operators . . .	260 (at 16) to		605

There is also a trainee administrator grade (the Junior Administrative Grade) which is only just now (1962) coming into use. The salary rates for this are: £620 to £775.

Appendix 2.ii

Number of Full-time Administrative and Clerical Staff
(England and Wales)

Grades	Sex(a)		Total(b)	%
	Male	Female		
Designated	1,795	18	1,813	5·6 ⎫
Senior Administrative . .	1,112	37	1,149	3·6 ⎬ 17·7
General Administrative . .	2,460	290	2,750	8·5 ⎭
Higher Clerical . . .	3,330	2,597	5,927	18·4 ⎫
Clerical	2,582	11,299	13,881	43·1 ⎬ 82·3
Sub-total	11,279	14,241	25,520	⎪
Typists and Machine Operators		6,691	6,691	20·8 ⎭
Total	11,279	20,932	32,211	
	35%	65%		100

There are also 1,337 part-time staff.

(a) The numbers of male and female in the designated and administrative grades are estimates based on our survey; the numbers in the Higher Clerical and Clerical grades are derived from the annual returns, SH6 and SH7. It has been assumed that all Typists and Machine Operators are female.

(b) The totals of staff by grades are derived from the Ministry of Health Annual Report, 1960, re-classified on the basis of additional information supplied by the Ministry.

Appendix 2.iii

Data relating to the four Regions surveyed and to England and Wales

	Region				Total	England & Wales (15 regions)
	Liverpool	North-East Met.	Sheffield	South Western	The four regions	
(a) Size (000 sq. miles to nearest quarter) .	¾	1½	6	7	15¼	58
(b) Population (millions)	2·2	3·3	4·7	2·9	13·1	45·8
(c) Available staffed beds	25,463	32,370	35,791	33,568	127,192	475,409
(d) Number of hospital authorities:						
i Regional Boards .	1	1	1	1	4	15
ii Boards of Governors	1	3	1	1	6	36
iii Hospital Management Committees	19	27	33	36	115	378
iv Total . . .	21	31	35	38	125	429
(e) Number of co-operating authorities .	19	30	35	38	122	—
(f) Total A & C staff (all authorities) . .	1,607	2,896	2,421	2,219	9,143	33,548
Part-time A & C staff (all authorities) .	54	251	158	67	530	1,337
Full-time A & C staff (all authorities) .	1,553	2,645	2,263	2,152	8,613	32,211
Full-time A & C staff (all authorities) (less typists & machine operators) . .	1,135	2,269	1,724	1,667	6,795	25,520
(g) Full-time A & C staff (less typists & machine operators in co-operating authorities	945	2,108	1,724	1,667	6,444	—

Sources: For (b) and (c)—'A Hospital Plan for England and Wales', Cmnd. 1604, H.M.S.O., January 1962.
For (d)—The Hospitals Year Book, 1962.
For (f) and (g)—Forms SH6 and SH7 and the Ministry of Health Annual Report 1960, H.M.S.O., July 1961. Cmnd. 1418.

Appendix 2.iv

Numbers of Full-time Administrative and Clerical Staff
(excluding Typists and Machine Operators) *of all Co-operating Authorities by Grades*

(a) = Number of staff according to annual returns SH6 and SH7. Copies of the questionnaire were sent to all of these.
(b) = Number who responded.
(c) = Percentage of response.

Grade	Liverpool (a)	(b)	(c)	North-East Metropolitan (a)	(b)	(c)	Sheffield (a)	(b)	(c)	South Western (a)	(b)	(c)	Total (a)	(b)	(c)
Males			%			%			%			%			%
D.1	7	5	71	7	6	86	10	5	50	6	4	67	30	20	67
D.2	26	20	77	40	31	78	48	28	59	51	41	80	165	120	73
D.3	42	25	60	83	52	63	86	58	67	66	55	83	277	190	69
Sub-total	75	50	67	130	89	68	144	91	63	123	100	81	472	330	70
SA	47	28	61	94	64	68	71	39	55	70	65	93	282	196	70
GA	83	54	64	215	116	54	184	105	57	191	158	83	673	433	64
HC	139	62	45	256	113	44	214	94	44	232	175	75	841	444	53
C	87	44	51	161	63	26	185	61	33	205	155	76	638	323	51
Total	431	238	55	856	445	52	798	390	49	821	653	80	2,906	1,726	59
Females			%			%			%			%			%
D.1	—	—	—	—	—	—	—	—	—	—	—	—	—	—	—
D.2	—	—	—	—	—	—	1	1	100	2	2	100	3	3	100
D.3	—	—	—	1	1	100	1	—	—	—	—	—	2	1	50
Sub-total	—	—	—	1	1	100	2	1	50	2	2	100	5	4	80
SA	1	1	100	3	2	67	4	2	50	1	1	100	9	6	67
GA	16	9	56	24	13	54	17	7	41	21	18	85	78	47	60
HC	108	46	43	243	89	37	131	52	40	170	123	72	652	310	48
C	389	120	31	981	189	19	772	237	31	652	443	68	2,794	989	35
Total	514	176	34	1,252	294	23	926	299	32	846	587	69	3,538	1,356	38

Appendix 3

Ages of Males by Grade

Age (years)	D.1	D.2	D.3	SA	GA	HC	C	Total
16							10	10
17							15	15
18						1	30	31
19						2	22	24
20							20	20
21						1	7	8
22						5	13	18
23						13	6	19
24					1	18	5	24
25					2	7	3	12
26					1	20	9	30
27					6	10	5	21
28				1	12	12	5	30
29				2	9	13	5	29
30				4	13	19	4	40
31				2	8	14	6	30
32		2	1	2	5	15	5	30
33				2	11	17	9	39
34				8	17	22	10	57
35		1	5	2	17	19	4	48
36			7	6	12	14	6	45
37		1	4	4	28	19	6	62
38	1	2	7	13	23	8	8	62
39		2	6	12	25	17	5	67
40		2	13	12	32	20	2	81
41		4	5	13	21	21	6	70
42		5	8	9	15	9	4	50
43	1	2	8	12	16	13	6	58
44		6	13	15	15	13	4	66
45		7	9	9	15	9	2	51
46		6	12	12	9	9	1	49
47	3	11	7	11	18	10	7	67
48	1	6	11	3	12	9	3	45
49	1	6	16	8	12	9	6	58
50		8	11	3	12	7	5	46
51	1	7	8	3	8	8	5	40
52	1	10	7	2	15	9	4	48
53	1	7	5	6	6	4	2	31
54		5	11	4	7	4	3	34
55	1	5	3	2	1	4	11	27
56	1	6		2	5	4	4	22
57		1	1	2	2	5	1	12
58	1	2	2	4	5	1	4	19
59	2	3	3		3	1	3	16
60	3		2		4	2		11
61	1		1	1	3	2	3	11
62	1		2	3	2	1	3	12
63		2	1	1	1	1	2	8
64		1	1		3	1	6	12
65+						2	8	10
Not Stated					1			1
Total	20	120	190	196	433	444	323	1,726

Appendix 4

Ages of Females by Grade

Age (years)				Grade				
	D.1	D.2	D.3	SA	GA	HC	C	Total
15							2	2
16							16	16
17							35	35
18							41	41
19							40	40
20							43	43
21						2	42	44
22							44	44
23						5	43	48
24						4	34	38
25						7	38	45
26						7	31	38
27						5	27	32
28						6	26	32
29					2	4	23	29
30					1	7	21	29
31					1	5	20	26
32					1	11	20	32
33					1	12	17	30
34					1	9	21	31
35						5	24	29
36					3	9	21	33
37					2	13	24	39
38					2	16	30	48
39				1	2	13	28	44
40					2	15	25	42
41						12	20	32
42				1	1	6	22	30
43						12	14	26
44					3	10	21	34
45			1		4	12	12	29
46				1	2	10	12	25
47				1	4	12	11	28
48						11	18	29
49				1	2	7	11	21
50		2		1	3	11	16	33
51					2	6	16	24
52					1	8	11	20
53						6	11	17
54					2	3	12	17
55					2	5	8	15
56						5	14	19
57					1	2	2	5
58						4	6	10
59						9	3	12
60		1			1	1	4	7
61					1	1		2
62							1	1
63							3	3
64							2	2
65+						1	2	3
Not Stated						1	1	2
Total		3	1	6	47	310	989	1,356

Appendix 5

No. of Staff Recruited each Year and the Ages at which they were Recruited (Males)

Year of entry	Annual Total	5-Year Total	14–	17–	20–	23–	26–	29–	32–	35–	38–	41–	44–	47–	50–	53–	56–	59–	62–	65–	Un-known
												Age-group at Entry (in years)									
1910																					
1																					
2																					
3	1	1	1																		
4																					
5	2																				
6	1																				
7		5	4	1																	
8	1																				
9	1																				
1920	9																				
1	9																				
2	6	37	12	16	5	3	1														
3	4																				
4	9																				
5	15																				
6	11																				
7	17	81	24	28	20	3	2	4													
8	17																				
9	21																				
1930	31																				
1	27																				
2	28	128	23	67	12	13	7	3	2		1										
3	23																				
4	19																				
5	25																				
6	29																				
7	29	143	35	58	15	12	9	5	2	4	2	1									
8	33																				
9	27																				
1940	19																				
1	16																				
2	14	74	20	24	4	1	5	4	4	2	4	2	2		2						
3	10																				
4	15																				
5	21																				
6	71																				
7	64	550	16	17	44	64	87	87	59	62	49	26	21	10	6		1				1
8	189																				
9	205																				
1950	114																				
1	68																				
2	44	294	14	11	41	45	33	41	25	21	23	16	8	3	3	4	5		1		
3	33																				
4	35																				
5	45																				
6	53																				
7	82	310	20	48	45	43	29	19	20	26	17	8	4	10	10	6	2	3			
8	61																				
9	69																				
1960	92	92	9	29	6	9	8	3	8	3	3	3	2	2	1	1	1	1	1	2	
Un-known	11																				11
Total	1,726		178	299	192	193	181	166	120	118	99	56	37	25	22	11	9	4	2	2	12

NOTE: See Appendix 7 for more detailed information concerning the years 1945–9.

Appendix 6

No. of Staff Recruited each Year and the Ages at which they were Recruited (Females)

Year of entry	Annual total	5-Year total	14–	17–	20–	23–	26–	29–	32–	35–	38–	41–	44–	47–	50–	53–	56–	Un-known
1918	1		1															
9	1	2		1														
1920	1																	
1	2																	
2		4	1	3														
3	1																	
4																		
5	3																	
6	2																	
7	2	14	4	9	1													
8	3																	
9	4																	
1930	3																	
1	6																	
2	3	18	3	9	2	3			1									
3	4																	
4	2																	
5	1																	
6	4																	
7	3	24	1	6	2	4	4	1	4		2							
8	6																	
9	10																	
1940	15																	
1	14																	
2	19	80	10	14	5	10	3	10	7	6	11	2		1				1
3	17																	
4	15																	
5	32																	
6	34																	
7	41	238	17	22	21	27	26	28	29	13	18	13	16	5	2	1		
8	65																	
9	66																	
1950	65																	
1	58																	
2	45	293	27	56	22	31	20	30	24	22	19	13	7	16	3	3		
3	51																	
4	74																	
5	86																	
6	81																	
7	83	500	45	122	62	43	26	31	40	44	29	20	17	14	5	1	1	
8	132																	
9	118																	
1960	158	158	14	49	27	18	7	11		7	9	7	7	1			1	
Un-known																		25
Total	1,356		123	291	142	136	86	111	105	92	88	55	47	37	10	5	2	26

NOTE: See Appendix 7 for more detailed information concerning the years 1945–9.

100

Appendix 7

(a) *No. of Staff Recruited during each of the Years* 1945–49 *and the Ages at which they were Recruited* (*Males*)

Year of entry	Annual total	5-Year total	14–	17–	20–	23–	26–	29–	32–	35–	38–	41–	44–	47–	50–	53–	56–	Un-known
1945	21		1	1			1	3	2	6	2	2		2	1			
6	71		6	2	4	9	20	10	5	7	4		3					1
7	64	550		2	9	22	6	11	5	2	1	1	2	3				
8	189		5	6	12	9	29	27	17	25	28	13	11	3	3		1	
9	205		4	6	19	24	31	36	30	22	14	10	5	2	2			
Total	550		16	17	44	64	87	87	59	62	49	26	21	10	6		1	1

(b) *No. of Staff Recruited during each of the Years* 1945–49 *and the Ages at which they were Recruited* (*Females*)

Year of entry	Annual total	5-Yr. total	14–	17–	20–	23–	26–	29–	32–	35–	38–	41–	44–	47–	50–	53–
1945	32		3	8	2	1	4	4	5	1		1	3			
6	34		4	1	6	6	3	5	2	1	1	2	1	2		
7	41	238	1	5	3	10	6	2	6		3	2	3			
8	65		6	5	3	5	4	7	8	6	9	4	5	3		
9	66		3	3	7	5	9	10	8	5	5	4	4		2	1
Total	238		17	22	21	27	26	28	29	13	18	13	16	5	2	1

Appendix 8

Ages on Promotion/Appointment to Present Grade (Males)

Age (years)	Grade						
	D.1	D.2	D.3	SA	GA	HC	C
15							3
16							30
17							34
18						2	31
19						1	11
20						5	10
21						4	6
22						15	9
23					2	25	13
24					5	25	7
25				1	5	14	5
26			2	1	10	21	9
27			1	2	10	13	9
28		1	1	3	16	10	5
29			3	4	18	13	6
30			2	5	16	15	6
31		1	3	10	15	15	7
32		4	2	7	24	10	2
33		5	5	10	23	16	6
34	1	2	7	16	22	11	6
35	2	5	17	11	14	18	6
36		6	14	12	16	9	4
37		10	25	13	18	11	4
38	2	8	18	12	13	8	2
39	1	14	14	7	17	8	8
40	1	6	17	9	14	6	7
41	1	11	10	10	8	6	5
42	1	6	4	8	9	8	2
43	1	10	11	6	6	6	4
44	1	6	6	5	6	6	4
45	2	5	8	5	7	4	3
46	1	4	5	1	10	1	6
47	2	5	6	3	1	5	6
48	2	3		1	4	2	2
49	2	1	3	1	3	2	4
50				2	4	1	5
51		2	1	2	6	2	3
52		1			4	1	2
53				1		1	3
54				1	1	2	4
55				2	1	2	4
56			1		2		3
57			1	1		2	1
58							1
59							3
60			1		2		1
61							1
62						2	1
63							1
64							
65							
66							2
Unknown		4	2	24	101	116	6
Total	20	120	190	196	433	444	323

Appendix 9

Ages on Promotion/Appointment to Present Grade (Females)

Age (years)	D.1	D.2	D.3	SA	GA	HC	C
					Grade		
14							2
15							15
16							68
17							79
18							80
19						2	51
20						1	43
21						3	38
22						8	37
23						9	25
24						8	35
25					1	5	23
26						4	21
27						6	18
28					4	7	17
29					2	5	30
30				1		7	23
31					1	5	17
32					2	9	18
33					3	11	22
34					2	13	18
35					2	5	18
36					1	13	19
37			1		2	15	18
38		2			1	13	28
39				1		6	21
40					1	4	15
41				1	2	4	13
42						1	17
43					2	4	7
44					1	7	15
45					1	8	9
46				1		4	11
47					1	5	9
48		1			2	4	12
49					1	3	6
50						2	7
51					1	3	
52						1	3
53						2	5
54							2
55						2	
Unknown				2	14	101	74
Total		3	1	6	47	310	989

*Pre-'N.H.S. Hospital Service' Employment (Males)**

Employment	Grade							
	D.1	D.2	D.3	SA	GA	HC	C	Total
No other employment .			1	6	12	38	76	133
Voluntary Hospitals etc. .	7	27	36	20	39	20	9	158
'Transferred' from Local Government . .	9	45	70	88	143	76	18	449
Local Government (other than above) and Civil Service . . .	4	34	58	38	91	84	44	353
Nationalized Industries (and predecessors). .		1	4	11	29	21	17	83
Private Industry/Commerce		6	13	17	71	130	98	335
Banking/Insurance . .		2			4	17	8	31
Employment in a professional office, etc. . . .		2	5	4	15	16	16	58
Other		2	2	10	20	28	22	84
Not Stated . . .		1	1	2	9	14	15	42
Total	20	120	190	196	433	444	323	1,726

Appendix 11

Pre-'N.H.S. Hospital Service' Employment (Females)*

Employment	Grade							
	D.1	D.2	D.3	SA	GA	HC	C	Total
No other employment .						19	177	196
Voluntary Hospitals etc. .		2		3	17	51	55	128
'Transferred' from Local Government . .		1		1	12	46	37	97
Local Government (other than above) and Civil Service . . .			1	2	3	41	98	145
Nationalized Industries (and predecessors). .						12	27	39
Private Industry/Commerce					6	77	313	396
Banking/Insurance . .					1	3	37	41
Employment in a professional office, etc. . . .					3	28	70	101
Other . . .					3	22	114	139
Not Stated . .					2	11	61	74
Total		3	1	6	47	310	989	1,356

* 'N.H.S. Hospital Service' refers solely to employment by an authority (e.g. R.H.B., B.G., H.M.C.) created by Part II of the National Health Service Act, 1946.

Persons employed in hospitals (or allied work) before the inception of the N.H.S. are shown above either as voluntary hospital officers or as Local Government Officers 'Transferred' in accordance with the provisions of the National Health Service Act, 1946 whichever is appropriate.

Appendix 12

Salary Structure

Present gross annual salary in £	Males		Females	
	Number of staff	*% of staff with salaries known*	*Number of staff*	*% of staff with salaries known*
0– 399	98	5·7	209	15·9
400– 599	116	6·9	475	36·1
600– 799	559	32·8	579	44·0
800– 999	306	18·0	33	2·5
1,000–1,199	243	14·3	13	1·0
1,200–1,399	130	7·6	2	·2
1,400–1,599	56	3·3	1	·1
1,600–1,799	51	3·0		
1,800–1,999	51	3·0	2	·2
2,000–2,199	29	1·7		
2,200–2,399	30	1·8	1	·1
2,400+	33	1·9		
Total of staff with salaries known . .	1,702	100	1,315	100
Salaries unknown .	24		41	
Total . .	1,726		1,356	

Appendix 13

Distribution of Male Staff in Administrative Divisions

Division	Grade							
	D.1	D.2	D.3	SA	GA	HC	C	*Total*
General Management	15	70	96	97	165	133	73	649
Finance . . .	5	34	62	49	163	188	89	590
Supplies . . .		8	28	21	48	32	24	161
Medical Records .				7	29	35	24	95
Medical Administration		1	2	1	3	3	1	11
Architects/Engineers .				2	4	15	11	32
Stores . . .					1	6	54	61
Establishments . .		1	1	6	3	3	1	15
Other . . .		5	1	11	14	12	11	54
Not Stated . .		1		2	3	17	35	58
Total . . .	20	120	190	196	433	444	323	1,726

Appendix 14

Distribution of Female Staff in Administrative Divisions

Division	Grade							
	D.1	D.2	D.3	SA	GA	HC	C	*Total*
General Management.		3		4	21	110	165	303
Finance . . .			1		7	56	106	170
Supplies . . .						2	21	23
Medical Records .				1	15	93	456	565
Medical Administration					1	16	6	23
Architects/Engineers .						3	14	17
Stores . . .						1	7	8
Establishments . .						2	3	5
Other . . .				1	3	13	92	109
Not Stated . .						14	119	133
Total . . .		3	1	6	47	310	989	1,356

These appendices give data of attempts by staff to move from one Hospital Authority to another since 1948.

Appendix 15

Applications Submitted (Males)
(a) *By Staff Recruited before* 1952

No. of applications	Grade							
	D.1	D.2	D.3	SA	GA	HC	C	Total
Nil	14	35	35	47	93	90	45	359
1		14	17	15	35	24	6	111
2		9	17	14	45	39	8	132
3		11	13	13	27	29	4	97
4	1	10	16	10	23	9	2	71
5		3	3	4	13	12	3	38
6	2	6	7	10	22	18		65
7	1	4	4	7	6	5	1	28
8		2	8	9	12	5	2	38
9		1	4	1	5			11
10		6	12	6	16	8		48
11				1	3	3		7
12	1	4	7	5	15	3		35
13				1	1	1		3
14			2		4	1		7
15		1	6	4	5	2		18
16			2		2			4
17				1	1	1		3
18				1	4	2		7
19				1				1
20		3	9	7	6	5	1	31
21–29	1	3	7	4	3	2		20
30–49		1	11	13	9	6	1	41
50–99			4	10	9	1		24
100–199					2			2
200					1			1
Total	20	113	184	184	362	266	73	1,202

(b) *By Staff Recruited during* 1952–55

No. of applications	D.1	D.2	D.3	SA	GA	HC	C	Total
Nil			2	3	3	21	23	52
1			1		4	7	7	19
2		1			4	9		14
3			1		5	7	6	19
4				1	3	9	4	17
5			1		1	5		7
6					2	4	3	9
7				1	2			3
8					1			1
9								
10					1	3		4
11–20				2	2	3		7
21–29								
30+				1	3	1		5
Total		1	5	8	31	69	43	157

(c) *By Staff Recruited since* 1955

No. of applications	D.1	D.2	D.3	SA	GA	HC	C	Total
Nil		4		3	17	54	158	236
1		1			5	16	19	41
2				1	3	15	10	29
3					3	9	7	19
4					5	1	4	10
5						7	1	8
6					3	1	1	5
7								
8						1		1
9								
10					1	2	1	4
11–20							2	2
21–29								
30–49								
50						1		1
		5		4	37	107	203	356

(d) *Staff Whose Year of Recruitment is Unknown*

No. of applications	Grade							
	D.1	D.2	D.3	SA	GA	HC	C	Total
Nil						1	4	5
1					1			1
2		1			2			3
3								
4								
5			1					1
6						1		1
		1	1		3	2	4	11

Appendix 16

Applications Submitted (Females)
(a) *By Staff Recruited before* 1952

No. of applications	Grade							
	D.1	D.2	D.3	SA	GA	HC	C	Total
Nil		2		5	21	135	190	353
1					6	24	28	58
2					5	16	17	38
3		1	1		1	7	7	17
4					2	7	1	10
5					1	3	5	9
6				1	1	4	1	7
7						2		2
8							1	1
9								
10								
11–20					3	2	1	6
21–29						1		1
30–49								
50–99							1	1
		3	1	6	40	201	252	503

(b) *By Staff Recruited during* 1952–55

No. of applications	Grade							
	D.1	D.2	D.3	SA	GA	HC	C	Total
Nil					3	41	154	198
1						11	25	36
2						5	1	6
3					1	3	7	11
4						1	2	3
5								
6						1		1
7								
8								
9								
10					1			1
					5	62	189	256

(c) *By Staff Recruited since 1955*

No. of applications	Grade							
	D.1	D.2	D.3	SA	GA	HC	C	Total
Nil					1	35	468	504
1					1	3	33	37
2						2	12	14
3						1	5	6
4						2	4	6
5								
6						2	1	3
7							1	1
8								
9						1		1
					2	46	524	572

(d) *Staff Whose Year of Recruitment is Unknown*

No. of applications	Grade							
	D.1	D.2	D.3	SA	GA	HC	C	Total
Nil						1	23	24
1								
2							1	1
						1	24	25

Appendix 17

Interviews Obtained (Males)

No. of Interviews	Grade							
	D.1	D.2	D.3	SA	GA	HC	C	Total
Nil	14	53	50	68	156	222	258	821
1	1	21	31	25	72	70	32	252
2	2	14	25	20	65	66	11	203
3		11	15	18	34	33	11	122
4		5	15	8	22	20	4	74
5		6	15	10	23	10	4	68
6	1	2	7	12	19	6	1	48
7		2	2	8	9	2		23
8		2	3	6	9	8		28
9	1		1	2	2			6
10		1	8	4	3	4	1	21
11			1	1				2
12		2	4	5	4	2		17
13			1		1			2
14			2	1	4			7
15			3	1	2		1	7
16	1	1	1					3
17					2			2
18			1	1				2
19								
20			1	1	4			6
21–30			3	4	2	1		10
31–40			1	1				2
	20	120	190	196	433	444	323	1,726

Appendix 18

Interviews Obtained (Females)

No. of interviews	Grade							
	D.1	D.2	D.3	SA	GA	HC	C	Total
Nil		3		5	28	225	864	1,125
1					9	44	70	123
2			1		4	15	31	51
3					1	10	14	25
4					1	9	5	15
5					1	3	2	6
6				1	1	2	3	7
7					1	1		2
8								
9					1			1
10–15						1		1
		3	1	6	47	310	989	1,356

Appendix 19

Appointments Obtained (Males)

No. of appointments	Grade							
	D.1	D.2	D.3	SA	GA	HC	C	Total
Nil	15	76	100	113	277	329	297	1,207
1	2	22	37	35	82	74	17	269
2	1	13	21	25	42	27	4	133
3		4	16	12	18	10	4	64
4	1	4	11	7	8	2		33
5	1	1	4	4	5		1	16
6			1			2		3
7					1			1
Total	20	120	190	196	433	444	323	1,726

Appendix 20

Appointments Obtained (Females)

No. of appointments	Grade							
	D.1	D.2	D.3	SA	GA	HC	C	*Total*
Nil		3		5	34	249	875	1,166
1			1		10	36	79	126
2					2	13	21	36
3					1	6	11	18
4				1		2	2	5
5						3		3
6						1	1	2
Total		3	1	6	47	310	989	1,356

Appendix 21

Marital Status and Age at Marriage (Males)

(a) Marital Status

Status	Grade							
	D.1	D.2	D.3	SA	GA	HC	C	Total
Married .	19	116	179	182	388	357	165	1,406
Single .		4	7	11	40	83	153	298
Widowed .	1		3	2	4	3	2	15
Divorced. .			1	1	1	1	3	7
Total . .	20	120	190	196	433	444	323	1,726

(b) Age at Marriage

Age (years)	Grade							
	D.1	D.2	D.3	SA	GA	HC	C	Total
18						1		1
19			1			4	1	6
20		1	1	1	6	3	1	13
21		4	5	11	10	19	13	62
22	1	5	6	14	31	25	10	92
23	1	8	16	11	31	29	17	113
24	4	12	20	15	42	58	14	165
25	3	12	25	16	59	41	17	173
26	2	15	23	24	41	44	16	165
27	4	16	25	23	38	33	16	155
28		4	12	18	32	16	12	94
29	2	9	14	17	22	18	8	90
30	1	8	7	8	13	19	14	70
31		9	5	6	15	9	5	49
32		3	5	6	9	7	5	35
33		1	5	3	12	5	4	30
34		3	2	2	4	4	1	16
35	1	3	2	4	7	8	2	27
36			3	2	3	2	3	13
37		1	1		3	6	1	12
38				1	3		1	5
39					1	1	1	3
40					1	1		2
41		1	1		1	1		4
42								
43			1	1	1	1	2	6
44	1			1				2
45		1			1	1		3
46					1		1	2
47								
48					1			1
49								
50								
51								
52			1		1			2
Not stated			2	1	4	4	5	17
Total	20	116	183	185	393	361	170	1,428

Appendix 22

Factors Affecting Mobility—Married (including Widowed and Divorced) Males

Factors	Grade							
	D.1	D.2	D.3	SA	GA	HC	C	*Total*
Housing	3	35	83	105	221	204	53	704
Children's Schooling . .	3	36	83	58	123	74	15	392
Dependent Relatives . .	2	14	35	22	56	54	14	197
Lack of Financial Incentive	3	32	77	94	181	146	61	594
Lack of Removal Allowance	1	16	37	57	128	90	17	346
Other Reasons . . .	1	21	23	27	62	29	24	187
Total Answers . . .	13	154	338	363	771	597	184	2,420
No. of Respondents . .	5	74	141	144	330	272	106	1,072
No. of Non-Respondents .	15	42	42	41	63	89	64	356
Total Staff . . .	20	116	183	185	393	361	170	1,428

Appendix 23

Factors Affecting Mobility—Single Males

Factors	Grade							
	D.1	D.2	D.3	SA	GA	HC	C	*Total*
Housing					4	7	4	15
Dependent Relatives . .		1		5	17	18	8	49
Lack of Financial Incentive		1	1	4	9	31	25	71
Lack of Removal Allowance				1	4	5	3	13
Other Reasons . . .		1	2	2	6	9	13	33
Total Answers . . .		3	3	12	40	70	53	181
No. of Respondents . .		2	3	9	24	45	43	126
No. of Non-Respondents .		2	4	2	16	38	110	172
Total Staff . . .		4	7	11	40	83	153	298

Appendix 24

Factors Affecting Mobility—Females

Factors	Grade							
	D.1	D.2	D.3	SA	GA	HC	C	*Total*
Housing		1		1	4	17	45	68
Children's Schooling . .				1	4	9	19	33
Dependent Relatives . .			1	2	11	59	69	142
Lack of Financial Incentive.		1			11	40	70	122
Lack of Removal Allowance		1			7	5	10	23
Other Reasons . . .				2	2	30	87	121
Total Answers . . .		3	1	6	39	160	300	509
No. of Respondents . .		1	1	4	26	129	220	381
No. of Non-Respondents .		2		2	21	181	769	975
Total Staff . . .		3	1	6	47	310	989	1,356

Appendix 25

Housing—Married (including Widowed and Divorced) Males

Nature of Accommodation	Grade							
	D.1	D.2	D.3	SA	GA	HC	C	*Total*
Buying (or completed buying) House/Flat . . .	18	92	135	125	256	208	75	909
Renting Council House/Flat		3	8	12	43	67	31	164
Renting Private House/Flat	1	9	23	29	53	64	50	229
Living in Lodgings . .			2	1		2	3	8
Living with Parents/Relations		1	1	6	8	8	7	31
Other	1	10	14	12	32	10	4	83
Not Stated . . .		1			1	2		4
Total	20	116	183	185	393	361	170	1,428

Appendix 26

Children of Males

(a) *Size of Family*

No. of children in family	Grade						
	D.1	D.2	D.3	SA	GA	HC	C
1	7	25	42	40	107	119	50
2	7	41	89	78	130	94	38
3	1	28	21	29	61	39	16
4	1	7	7	4	16	8	5
5	1		1	2	3	2	
6	1				2		
None	2	15	23	32	74	99	61
Total married etc.* Males . .	20	116	183	185	393	361	170
Total children .	39	219	316	309	641	466	194
Average No. of children per family	2·0	1·9	1·7	1·7	1·6	1·3	1·1

* 'Married etc.' includes widowed and divorced persons.

(b) *Ages of Children*

Age Groups (years)	Grade							
	D.1	D.2	D.3	SA	GA	HC	C	*Total*
0–5	2	20	48	56	167	151	41	485
6–10	1	31	61	84	189	125	24	515
11–15	10	65	102	99	150	98	36	560
16+	26	103	105	70	135	92	93	624
Total	39	219	316	309	641	466	194	2,184

Appendix 27

Marital Status and Children of Females
(a) Marital Status

Status	Grade							
	D.1	D.2	D.3	SA	GA	HC	C	*Total*
Married . .				1	4	87	363	455
Single . .		3	1	4	37	185	561	791
Widowed .				1	4	20	45	70
Divorced .					2	18	18	38
Not Stated .							2	2
Total . .		3	1	6	47	310	989	1,356

(b) Size of Family

No. of children in family	Grade						
	D.1	D.2	D.3	SA	GA	HC	C
1					5	36	96
2				1	1	16	69
3						4	21
4						1	6
None				1	4	68	234
Total married etc.* Females . .				2	10	125	426
Total children .				2	7	84	321

* 'Married etc.' includes widowed and divorced persons.

(c) Ages of Children

Age groups (*years*)	Grade							
	D.1	D.2	D.3	SA	GA	HC	C	*Total*
0–5					1	3	15	19
6–10						8	40	48
11–15				1	2	19	96	118
16+				1	4	54	170	229
Total				2	7	84	321	414

Appendix 28

Career Expectations (*Males*)

Expectation	Grade						
	D.1	D.2	D.3	SA	GA	HC	C
Chief Administrative/Finance Supplies Officer	11	87	139	87	91	38	62
Designated Officer (other than above)		9	38	79	116	62	17
Senior Administrative Grade				27	161	108	54
General Administrative Grade					58	155	63
Higher Clerical (or equivalent) Grade						62	68
Clerical (or equivalent) Grade						2	30
Not Stated	9	24	13	3	7	17	29
Total	20	120	190	196	433	444	323

Appendix 29

Preparedness to Move to Any Part of the Country
(a) *By Married Males*

Mobility	Grade							
	D.1	D.2	D.3	SA	GA	HC	C	*Total*
Prepared . .	3	29	54	69	126	137	68	486
Not prepared .	14	80	125	113	261	218	89	900
Not stated .	3	7	4	3	6	6	13	42
Total . .	20	116	183	185	393	361	170	1,428

(b) *By Single Males*

Mobility	Grade							
	D.1	D.2	D.3	SA	GA	HC	C	*Total*
Prepared . .		2	1	3	18	41	96	161
Not prepared .		1	6	8	21	41	54	131
Not stated .		1			1	1	3	6
Total . .		4	7	11	40	83	153	298

Appendix 30

Employment of Wives

Employment	Grade							
	D.1	D.2	D.3	SA	GA	HC	C	*Total*
Not working . . .	17	104	144	125	262	197	89	938
Full-time employment .	1	2	10	28	60	85	48	234
Part-time employment .	1	9	25	28	65	69	24	221
Not applicable (in the case of widowed or divorced persons . . .	1		4	3	5	5	5	23
Not stated . . .		1		1	1	5	4	12
Total, married etc. Males .	20	116	183	185	393	361	170	1,428

Appendix 31

Nature of Full-time Education Received (*Males*)

Type of school etc.	Grade							
	D.1	D.2	D.3	SA	GA	HC	C	*Total*
Elementary . . .	4	10	17	19	58	79	71	258
Private . . .		2	2	1	9	18	13	45
Secondary Modern								
(or equivalent)		1	13	14	38	55	43	164
Technical/Commercial .		8	10	13	52	37	40	160
Grammar (or equivalent) .	10	72	123	121	246	223	134	929
Public (i.e. 'Headmasters'								
Conference' School) .	4	17	18	16	20	22	15	112
University . . .	2	8	6	10	9	7	4	46
Other				1	1		1	3
Unknown . . .		2	1	1		3	2	9
Total	20	120	190	196	433	444	323	1,726

Appendix 32

Nature of Full-time Education Received (*Females*)

Type of school etc.	Grade						
	D.1	D.2	D.3	SA	GA	HC	C	*Total*
Elementary . . .					3	38	84	125
Private . . .		1			4	32	82	119
Secondary Modern								
(or equivalent)					2	29	146	177
Technical/Commercial .		1		1	7	52	175	236
Grammar (or equivalent) .		1	1	4	21	148	465	640
Public (i.e. 'Headmasters'								
Conference' School) .					3	9	23	35
University . . .				1	6	1	4	12
Other							3	3
Unknown . . .					1	1	7	9
Total		3	1	6	47	310	989	1,356

Appendix 33

Nature of Education Undertaken Since Working Career Commenced
(Males)

Type of Education	Grade							
	D.1	D.2	D.3	SA	GA	HC	C	*Total*
University:								
Full-time . . .		3		5	4			12
Part-time . . .	3	21	25	15	20	14	7	105
Tech./Commercial College:								
Full-time . . .		3	3	3	10	7	8	34
Part-time . . .	10	68	123	110	225	210	157	903
Correspondence Courses .	11	89	143	146	260	212	93	954
Other	3	10	9	12	41	36	30	141
Number of Courses of Study undertaken . . .	27	194	303	291	560	479	295	2,149
Participants in the above Courses . . .	15	112	176	179	380	338	229	1,429
Non-Participants . .	5	8	14	17	53	106	94	297
Total	20	120	190	196	433	444	323	1,726

Appendix 34

Nature of Education Undertaken Since Working Career Commenced
(Females)

Type of Education	Grade							
	D.1	D.2	D.3	SA	GA	HC	C	Total
University:								
Full-time				1				1
Part-time				1	6	9	12	28
Tech./Commercial College:								
Full-time					5	16	55	76
Part-time		3	1	2	20	160	453	639
Correspondence Courses		1	1		12	38	45	97
Other		1			5	23	80	109
Number of Courses of Study undertaken		5	2	4	48	246	645	950
Participants in the above Courses		3	1	4	33	206	577	824
Non-Participants				2	14	104	412	532
Total		3	1	6	47	310	989	1,356

Appendix 35

Basic Educational Attainments (Males)

Examinations	Grade							
	D.1	D.2	D.3	SA	GA	HC	C	Total
G.C.E.:								
'A' Level (and equivalents)	1	6	11	17	26	26	16	103
'O' Level—Five or more subjects (and equivalents)	12	82	110	108	196	149	63	720
'O' Level—Less than five subjects		1	6	10	15	48	83	163
Other Examinations of similar standard	1	6	17	15	46	27	16	128
Nil	6	25	46	46	150	194	145	612
Total	20	120	190	196	433	444	323	1,726

Appendix 36

Basic Educational Attainments (Females)

Examinations	Grade							
	D.1	D.2	D.3	SA	GA	HC	C	*Total*
G.C.E. :								
'A' Level (and equivalents)				1	4	7	24	36
'O' Level—Five or more subjects (and equivalents)		1	1	3	20	106	260	391
'O' Level—Less than five subjects . .						11	138	149
Other Examinations of similar standard . .		1		1	5	25	50	82
Nil		1		1	18	161	517	698
Total		3	1	6	47	310	989	1,356

Appendix 37

University and Professional Examinations (Males)
(a) *Designated Officers*

Examining Body	Studying for:		Passed Inter-mediate (and no longer studying)	Passed Final etc.
	Intermediate	Final		
University:				
Degrees	3	1	9	23
Diplomas			2	39
Professional:				
I.H.A.			1	220
C.I.S. . .		1	11	29
C.C.S. . .		1		30
I.M.T.A. .			12	33
C.A.;A.C.C.A.;⎱ C.W.A. . .⎰		1	4	50
A.M.R.O. ⎱ Inst. P.S. ⎰				10
Other. . .			3	41
Total . .	3	4	42	475
	Total Qualified/Studying		294	
	Others		36	
	Total Staff		330	

Examining Body	Studying for		Passed Intermediate (and no longer studying)	Passed Final etc.
	Intermediate	*Final*		
University:				
Degrees . .	1	1	5	17
Diplomas .			8	22
Professional:				
I.H.A. . .	21	23	20	151
C.I.S. . .	3	5	22	19
C.C.S . .	3	3	4	17
I.M.T.A. .		4	9	2
C.A.;A.C.C.A.; } C.W.A. . . }	4	5	13	22
A.M.R.O. } Inst. P.S. } .	3	2	1	14
Other. . .	1	1	6	41
Total . .	36	44	88	305

Total Qualified/Studying	367	
Others	262	
Total Staff	629	

(c) *Higher Clerical and Clerical Grades*

Examining Body	Studying for:		Passed Intermediate (and no longer studying)	Passed Final etc.
	Intermediate	Final		
University:				
Degrees . .		1	2	5
Diplomas .	1		5	2
Professional:				
I.H.A. . .	68	12	4	12
C.I.S. . .	7	1	3	2
C.C.S. . .	2	8	2	2
I.M.T.A. .	5			
C.A.; A.C.C.A.; C.W.A. . .	8	5	5	3
A.M.R.O. Inst. P.S. .	3		1	2
Other. . .	2		3	11
Total . .	96	27	25	39

Total Qualified/Studying	168
Others	599
Total Staff	767

Summary

	D.1, 2 and 3	SA and GA	HC and C	Total
Total Qualified/Studying	294	367	168	829
Others . . .	36	262	599	897
Total Staff . .	330	629	767	1,726

Appendix 38

University and Professional Examinations (Females)
(a) *Designated Officers, Senior and General Administrative Grades*

Examining Body	Studying for		Passed Intermediate (and no longer studying)	Passed Final etc.
	Intermediate	Final		
University:				
Degrees . .				2
Diplomas .		1		4
Professional:				
I.H.A. . .			1	7
C.I.S. . .				2
C.C.S. . .		1		
I.M.T.A. .				1
C.A.; A.C.C.A.; ⎫				1
C.W.A. . ⎭				
A.M.R.O. ⎫ .				9
Inst. P.S. ⎭				
Other . . .				3
Total . .		2	1	29

Total Qualified/Studying   27
Others   30
Total Staff   57

(b) *Higher Clerical and Clerical Grades*

Examining Body	Studying for:		Passed Intermediate (and no longer studying)	Passed Final etc.
	Intermediate	*Final*		
University:				
Degrees . .			3	2
Diplomas .	1		1	3
Professional:				
I.H.A. . .	4	2	2	3
C.I.S. . .	2		1	
C.C.S. . .				3
I.M.T.A.				
C.A.;A.C.C.A.;⎫				
C.W.A. .⎬	1			
A.M.R.O. ⎫				
Inst. P.S. ⎬ ·	3			7
Other. . .			1	9
Total . .	11	2	8	27

Total Qualified/Studying	43
Others	1,256
Total Staff	1,299

Summary

	D.1, 2 and 3, SA and GA	HC and C	Total
Total Qualified/Studying	27	43	70
Others . . .	30	1,256	1,286
Total Staff . .	57	1,299	1,356

NOTE: Abbreviations used:

I.H.A.	—	Institute of Hospital Administrators
C.I.S.	—	Chartered Institute of Secretaries
C.C.S.	—	Corporation of Certified Secretaries
I.M.T.A.	—	Institute of Municipal Treasurers and Accountants
C.A.	—	Institute of Chartered Accountants
A.C.C.A.	—	Association of Certified and Corporate Accountants
C.W.A.	—	Association of Cost and Works Accountants
A.M.R.O.	—	Associations of Medical Records Officers
Inst. P.S.	—	Institute of Public Supplies Officers

131

Appendix 39

Effects of World War II on Education and Professional Training (Males)

Whether or not adversely affected	*Grade*							
	D.1	D.2	D.3	SA	GA	HC	C	*Total*
Yes . . .	8	52	102	131	244	198	143	878
No . . .	12	65	87	63	182	222	135	766
Not Stated .		3	1	2	7	24	45	82
Total . .	20	120	190	196	433	444	323	1,726

Appendix 40

Effects of World War II on Education and Professional Training (Females)

Whether or not adversely affected	*Grade*							
	D.1	D.2	D.3	SA	GA	HC	C	*Total*
Yes . . .		1			9	49	127	186
No . . .		2	1	6	35	241	728	1,013
Not Stated .					3	20	134	157
Total . .		3	1	6	47	310	989	1,356

Appendix 41

Participation in Vocational Courses and Training Schemes (Males)

Type of Course	Grade							
	D.1	D.2	D.3	SA	GA	HC	C	*Total*
King's Fund Bursaries or 2-year Course . . .		3	2	5	4			14
King's Fund Administrative Staff College Courses .	5	24	33	18	5	1		86
Leeds University Pilot Scheme		6	3	14	15	2		40
National Training Scheme .				1	3			4
N.A.L.G.O. Schools, etc. .	2	12	21	30	41	29	11	146
I.H.A. Schools, etc. . .	4	24	50	45	58	31	8	220
Regional Training Schemes .	1	2	5	16	26	10	3	63
Board of Governors/H.M.C. Training Schemes . .	2		2	8	9	11	10	42
Other.	1	7	13	14	27	10	5	77
Total Courses attended .	15	78	129	151	188	94	37	692
Number of Participants .	9	55	90	103	141	74	36	508
Number of Non-Participants	11	65	100	93	292	370	287	1,218
Total Staff	20	120	190	196	433	444	323	1,726

Appendix 42

Participation in Vocational Courses and Training Schemes (Females)

Type of Course	Grade							
	D.1	D.2	D.3	SA	GA	HC	C	*Total*
King's Fund Bursaries or 2-year Course . . .								
King's Fund Administrative Staff College Courses .				1	1	1		3
Leeds University Pilot Scheme				1	1	2		4
National Training Scheme .								
N.A.L.G.O. Schools, etc. .			1	1	3	8	7	20
I.H.A. Schools, etc. . .		2		1	6	6	1	16
Regional Training Schemes .				1	7	3	5	16
Board of Governors/H.M.C. Training Schemes . .				1	1	1	3	6
Other.			1	1	9	9	11	31
Total Courses attended .		2	2	7	28	30	27	96
Number of Participants .		2	1	4	19	25	27	78
Number of Non-Participants		1		2	28	285	962	1,278
Total Staff		3	1	6	47	310	989	1,356

Appendix 43

Anticipated Year of Retirement (Males)

Year	D.1	D.2	D.3	SA	GA	HC	C	Total
1960					1			1
1	1			1	4	3	8	17
2	1	7	6	2	3	1	4	24
3	3	2	2	5	2	2	3	19
4	1	3	1	2	4	2	3	16
5	2	4	5		5	4	2	22
6		5	9	4	7	3	3	31
7	2	5	2	2	8		3	22
8	1	7	4	3	8	6	1	30
9	1	3	3	4	3	3	2	19
1970		7	8	3	8	10	12	48
1		5	15	6	10	6	6	48
2		8	4	7	6	9	4	38
3	1	11	7	9	16	9	4	57
4	1	5	10	5	6	7	6	40
5		11	12	7	17	10	9	66
6	1	8	12	14	9	8	4	56
7	2	3	13	10	14	10	1	53
8	2	3	10	7	17	9	7	55
9		6	6	8	17	5	2	44
1980		2	14	6	23	11	3	59
1		3	6	15	21	17	2	64
2	1	2	6	8	15	9	4	45
3		1	4	4	15	12	4	40
4		2	6	10	17	19	4	58
5			4	12	27	23	4	70
6		2	5	10	20	16	3	56
7		1	5	8	15	12	10	51
8		2	3	2	16	19	6	48
9				5	9	17	9	40
1990		1	5	2	20	31	6	65
1			1	5	11	21	8	46
2				1	13	15	8	37
3			1	1	6	8	5	22
4				2	6	9	5	22
5				3	9	12	6	30
6				1	8	9	3	21
7				1	8	14	7	30
8					4	6	7	17
9					1	14	9	24
2000						9	4	13
1					1	15	10	26
2						6	6	12
3						5	14	19
4							4	4
5							16	16
6						1	16	17
7						1	24	25
8							9	9
9							5	5
2010							4	4
Not stated			1	1	3	6	14	25
Total	20	120	190	196	433	444	323	1,726

135

Appendix 44

Anticipated Year of Retirement (Females)

Year	Grade							
	D.1	D.2	D.3	SA	GA	HC	C	Total
1960							7	7
1						11	24	35
2						7	19	26
3				1	1	6	19	27
4					1	6	18	25
5		1			1	5	33	40
6					1	4	18	23
7						6	8	14
8					1	7	18	26
9					3	5	13	21
1970		2		1	5	12	29	49
1					2	9	10	21
2					1	7	22	30
3					4	5	10	19
4				1	2	9	10	22
5			1		4	12	12	29
6				2	2	11	14	29
7						11	9	20
8				1	1	12	14	28
9					1	5	13	19
1980					1	19	25	45
1					1	5	15	21
2					2	14	26	42
3					2	9	20	31
4					1	4	14	19
5					2	7	15	24
6					1	6	12	19
7						8	11	19
8					1	7	14	22
9						3	12	15
1990					1	2	19	22
1					2	3	9	14
2					1	3	10	14
3						6	10	16
4					1	3	12	16
5						2	14	16
6					1	2	15	18
7						2	16	18
8							21	21
9							18	18
2000						2	17	19
1							15	15
2							17	17
3							17	17
4							10	10
5							4	4
6							4	4
7							3	3
8							1	1
9							1	1
Not Stated						53	272	325
Total		3	1	6	47	310	989	1,356

Appendix 45

Method of Calculating Career Prospects

Vide Chapter 7 (page 68 *et seq.*)

These calculations are based upon the assumptions about an even age-structure and promotion ages referred to in our text. We also assume that many staff will work until they are 65.

To arrive at the figures of 67, 39, 78, 82 and 17 shown on page 68 take the number of posts in each grade and the promotion ages shown on the same page.

The working-span in the designated grades will be $65 - 38 = 27$ years. With an even age-structure this will provide $1,813 \div 27 = 67$ job opportunities in the designated grades each year.

The median promotion-age to the SA grade is 37. Since the 67 designated officers will in many cases have worked their way through the SA grade, 37 posts each year in the SA grade will be occupied by the prospective designated officers. The remainder, $1,149—67 = 1,082$, will be occupied by the staff who will work in this grade from 37 to 65, i.e. 28 years. This number divided into 1,082 gives the approximate number of job opportunities in the SA grade each year, i.e. 39. The median promotion-age to the GA grade is 34. Since the 67 designated officers and 39 SA staff will usually have worked their way through the GA grade over a 'theoretical' working-span of $37 - 34 = 3$ years in the GA grade, then $(67 + 39) \times 3$ posts in the GA grade will be occupied by prospective designated officers and SA staff. The remaining posts 2,432, i.e. $2,750 - 3 (67 + 39)$ will be occupied by staff who will work in this grade from 34 to 65, i.e. 31 years. This number divided into 2,432 gives the approximate number of job opportunities in the GA grade each year, i.e. 78.

Similar calculations produce the figures of 82 and 17 for the Higher Clerical and Clerical grades respectively.

Appendix 46

Staff Wastage in the Civil Service

Staff wastage (i.e. losses in a labour force other than from retirals at normal retirement ages) can be calculated only if staff records have been maintained over many years. For the reasons we have explained (page 2) such records have not been kept in the hospital service.

The Establishment (Management) Division of H.M. Treasury have kindly supplied us with the following statistics relating to staff wastage of General Executive (male) staff in the Civil Service.

Age (years)	Years (% p.a.)		
	1959	1960	1961
—19	29·7	18·2	21·3
20	8·6	7·3	10·2
21	26·1	6·6	9·0
22	7·4	7·0	6·0
23	2·8	4·1	3·4
24	3·2	2·2	4·3
25	2·2	2·0	3·3
26	1·6	1·9	1·7
27	3·4	1·0	0
28	·9	0	1·4
29	·9	·8	1·2
30	1·7	·8	1·7

For both male and female General Executive staff the average wastage per annum over the three years 1959–61 was:

	%
Staff under age 30	6·6
Ages 30–49	·8
Ages 50–59	1·9
Over age 60	25·5

These figures relate to a much larger labour force than in comparable grades of staff in the hospital service and, in our view, there is probably a smaller drift of male staff out of the hospital service.